DAUGHTER OF
JERUSALEM

JOANNE OTTO

Daughter of Jerusalem

For additional titles by Joanne Otto visit:
www.joanneotto.com

Published by:

Divine Purpose Publishing, LLC
P.O. Box 471004, Celebration, FL. 34747
www.divinepurposepublishing.com

Library of Congress Control Number: 2018945987
Print ISBN-13: 978-0-9996-8478-8
Amazon Print ISBN-13: 978-1-9488-1216-0
ePub ISBN: 978-1-9488-1201-6

Printed in the United States of America

To all who love Yeshua

CONTENTS

PREFACE

The story of my young Jewish heroine's encounters with Jesus began to come alive in my imagination several decades ago. As often occurs, however, with important but not urgent projects, the writing of it got buried under daily happenings. Fast forward to 2009 when I found myself sharing the story with my daughter Meghan Williams. She looked at me and said, with a passionate conviction that took my breath away, "Mom, you have got to write that book!"

From that moment I became a woman with a mission, but after almost three years of research and note taking, the creative spark I needed to actually tell the story seemed all but extinguished. Then one morning I awoke and placed my little book entirely in God's hands. I didn't care who got credit for writing it. I just wanted it to be out there and to bless. It was then that I realized I knew a writer who would love the story as I did and might help me tell it: Angela Sage Larsen. I called her, and we discussed the project over lunch. She was most encouraging but told me that a book contract would prevent her from being actively involved until the following year. When I asked her what I should be doing in the meantime, she replied, "Write me an outline of the story." To my amazement, that outline grew to eleven pages. The spark had been relit! In less than six months, I had completed the first draft of the manuscript.

Rather than being my co-author, Angela graciously became my coach through the many details leading up to publication. Meanwhile, my daughter Meghan designed the book's beautiful cover, which includes a model of the Temple as it would have looked in Jesus' time with the Antonia Fortress on the far right. During the final stages of the project, I also had the invaluable help of my insightful and tireless editor, Trudy Palmer. Besides these three essential helpers, I was blessed with a number of supportive friends who read the manuscript from the perspective of a teenager, a Bible scholar, an educator, a writing coach, a Christian, or a Jew, sharing helpful feedback. To all of them, my heartfelt thanks.

Thanks also to you, dear reader, for your interest. You have in your hands a book that can be for you whatever you choose. You can just enjoy it as a story. Or if you are also interested in the story behind the story—in the remarkable world in which Jesus lived and in the biblical foundations on which the story rests—the appendix at the back will help you explore Jesus' world further.

For every chapter that refers directly to the Bible, you will find the books, chapters, and verses from which these references are drawn, listed in the order in which they appear in the chapter. (Versions of the same story told in two or more Gospels are grouped on the same line. You will also find questions about that chapter to think about and perhaps discuss with your family, friends, or Bible study group. In the glossary, you will find short, simple explanations for twenty words—mostly Hebrew ones—that you may not have encountered before or may wish to know more about.

These resources are, of course, just a start. The possibilities for further discovery in books and on the Internet are endless. Whatever direction your journey with *Daughter of Jerusalem* takes, may it be a blessed and satisfying one.

Joanne Otto

INTRODUCTION

Have you ever wondered what it would have been like to meet Jesus face to face? If so, prepare to embark on an imaginative journey to a time and place very different from our own.

You'll find yourself in a far corner of the Roman Empire known as Palestine around the year 30 AD. There are no Christian churches. In fact, no one has even been called a Christian yet. Believers in the one God are of the Jewish faith, and to them the holiest place of all is the city of Jerusalem. Each year thousands of Jews, including Jesus himself, travel to Jerusalem for the holy festivals. And the most important festival of all is Passover, which celebrates their liberation under Moses' leadership from slavery in Egypt. Passover brings so many Jews to Jerusalem that its population doubles.

If you, too, have traveled to Jerusalem for a festival, you might see a crowd gathering around Jesus as he teaches in Solomon's portico, which rims the Temple's outer court, or on the steps leading to its entrance through the Huldah Gates. You might edge closer to him through the crowd to hear what he is saying. He is speaking in Aramaic, a language similar to

Hebrew. The name he is known by is also Aramaic: Yeshua. He comes from Nazareth in Galilee, a place that anyone from Jerusalem would consider terribly backward. He probably even speaks with a Galilean accent. But people are drawn to him nevertheless.

What if one of those people is a girl of about fourteen years? What does she think of this young rabbi from Galilee? How will her encounters with him influence her life?

1

Jericho, summer of 3789 (29 AD)

Mara takes a deep breath as she escapes through the open door and slips out into the courtyard. She feels somewhat guilty, but she cannot help herself. She simply has to escape from her sister Rachel's marriage feast.

The loud, rhythmic bursts of music and the strident voices of the wedding guests seem to be in competition with each other. And the air inside, already unbearably hot, has become thick and stuffy from the smoke of the oil lamps. If only Rachel's marriage could have been celebrated in Jerusalem instead of down here in Jericho! Up in the hills, there might at least have been a breeze.

In the light of a nearly full moon, Mara looks out across the flat, arid landscape skirting the western side of Jericho to the rocky hills where the road back to Jerusalem awaits her. She is eager to escape Jericho's stifling heat, but not at all eager to leave Rachel behind. Mara can hardly imagine her life back in Jerusalem without Rachel's peaceful smile and helping hands. From now on there will be no one to deflect their mother's ceaseless demands for help. Only Mara will be at hand—Mara, who would far rather be reading and discussing the Torah with her father than doing housework.

If only she were a boy. Then her interest in the holy books would be encouraged and respected. As a girl, all that lies ahead for her is marriage to someone she may not even like—and then children who will take up every moment of her time that is not spent keeping house.

At least Mara can be thankful that today is Rachel's wedding day and not her own. But sixteen-year-old Rachel, only two years older than Mara, is marrying later than many girls do. How long can Mara hope to postpone her own wedding? It astounds her that Rachel seems so contented with her lot. It must be because she actually cares for Matthias. For that she may have their father to thank. He had been exceptionally kind in turning down two reasonable marriage proposals for Rachel before accepting the one from Matthias. Few brides are so fortunate. Mara wonders whether he will be as patient with her.

Her musing ends abruptly when a tall robed figure emerges from the house. It is her father, Eleazar. His craggy, bearded face looks almost forbidding in the moonlight until he is close enough for Mara to catch sight of his kindly eyes.

"So, Mara, what brings you out here?" he asks. "Your mother and sister are worried about you. I, of course, know you better." And he grins at her—rather boyishly, she thinks, for a man of such dignity.

"I do not see how people can bear it in there," Mara replies. "It is far too hot and stuffy for *me*. Besides, this whole day has given me a great deal to think about."

"So, what has been the object of your thoughts, dear Daughter?"

"I was just wishing I were a boy," she confesses. Then, looking up into her father's eyes, she asks, "You have always wanted a son, haven't you? And HaShem gave you only Rachel and me."

"Make no mistake, Mara. I would not exchange either of you —not even for a son."

"I know that, Abba," she assures him, "but I also know that Ima will need my help now more than ever. When will I have even a moment for our Torah studies?"

"Ah, so then you would really miss them?"

"Oh, Abba, you *know* that!" she shoots back in exasperation.

"I always thought you were just looking for a good reason to stay away from the kitchen."

Mara glances up at him in disbelief. Yes, there is just a hint of a smile. "That is certainly what Ima thinks," she says. "Besides, she is convinced that Torah study is suitable only for men and boys."

"And many women would agree with her," Eleazar observes.

"But what do *you* think, Abba?" asks Mara, gazing expectantly into his eyes.

"Well, Mara, I must confess that ten or fifteen years ago I would have agreed with her, too," her father admits. "But then a small miracle happened under my own roof. I knew from the day of your birth that I would probably never have a son—that your mother could bear me no more children. To me it meant that the holy books to which I had devoted my life were never to be shared with a child of my own. It saddened me, but I was resigned to it. Till one day …"

"Was it the day you read me the story of how the waters parted and Moses led the children of Israel across the Red Sea?" Mara asks.

"It was," Eleazar replies. "And then you wanted to hear more stories from the Torah and from the histories of the kings. Soon you were able to read them yourself, so we spent more and more of our time discussing them ... just as I would have with a son."

"Yes, I have always loved those stories about our people," Mara reflects, "but since last year I have also come to love the *laws* HaShem has given us. Think how lost we would be without them in a world ruled by these Romans with their graven images!"

"Very true. So you would like to learn more?" There, once again, is that whisper of a grin.

"As if you were not aware of that!" Mara retorts. "But what about Ima and all the work that Rachel will not be able to do for her anymore?"

"I suppose your mother and I will just have to reach an agreement," he replies. "I will permit you to be a daughter to her so long as she permits you to be a 'son' to me. It seems only reasonable."

He puts an arm around her shoulders and shepherds her back toward the door she had escaped through only minutes before. The room is still hot and stuffy and noisy, but somehow it no longer feels like a prison.

2

Jerusalem, the following autumn

"*Shema Yisrael, Adonai elohenu Adonai ehad.*" ("Hear, O Israel, the Lord our God is one Lord.") These words and those that follow them in the fifth Book of Moses are as essential to the rhythm of Mara's day as dawn and sunset. In Eleazar ben Judah's household, as in every other worshipful Jewish home, this affirmation of the Lord's oneness begins and ends each day.

And just as the *Shema* gives shape and meaning to the day, the holy festivals give shape and meaning to the year. Mara especially enjoys the one they are celebrating now: *Sukkot*, the Feast of the Tabernacles. During this festival, her family, like all devout Jewish families, commemorates the forty years when the Israelites lived in tents while on their way from Egypt to the Promised Land. For seven days they take their meals—and in most cases even sleep—in a *sukkah*, a booth with a roof made of leafy boughs. In a city like Jerusalem, many sukkahs, including Eleazar's, are constructed on the flat, walled rooftops of the houses. This holiday can be a time of adventure and family closeness as well as a time of prayer and praise.

But the elements can alter that. Rain, heavy winds, or extreme temperatures can make Sukkot a trial. At those times, her father never fails to point out that these conditions only help them better appreciate what their ancestors endured. But under such circumstances, Mara finds it difficult to appreciate much of anything, so she is grateful that, thus far, the weather during this year's festival has been nearly perfect.

This afternoon her parents are paying a traditional holiday visit to another couple—a fellow member of the *Sanhedrin* and his wife. Perhaps some confidential matters will be discussed. At least, Mara guesses that may be the case since she was not asked to join them. But she is not at all disappointed because it will give her time to take a closer look at the Torah scroll her father was poring over the previous evening.

She has been studying it for only a few minutes, however, when a shadow falls across the passage she is reading. She looks up to see her tousled-haired, fun-loving friend Nathan whom the years of familiarity have all but turned into a brother, standing in the doorway that leads to the courtyard between their family homes.

With an unusually serious expression on his face, he asks her a question she will remember for the rest of her life: "Mara, have you heard of a young Galilean rabbi named Yeshua?"

"No, I have not," she replies. "How would I hear about someone who is way up in Galilee?"

"People here are talking about him," Nathan explains. "He has done some remarkable things."

"Such as?"

"Well, for one thing, he fed a huge crowd of people—over five thousand—with just five barley loaves and a few little fish.

And he heals people—sick ones, crippled ones, blind ones. He even does it on the Sabbath."

"How can he be a good Jew if he breaks the Sabbath?" Mara asks doubtfully.

"I cannot answer that, Mara," Nathan replies. "I know Yeshua only by hearsay. But I am told that he is here in Jerusalem for the festival, and I am hoping to hear him teach. Would you like to join me?"

Without a moment's hesitation, Mara reaches for her shawl, and she and Nathan are soon making their way along the crowded, narrow streets, heading toward the Temple, where Yeshua has reportedly been seen. While they walk, Nathan, who still is not quite convinced that a woman can be a real Torah scholar, is once again playing his favorite game of attempting to find some gap in Mara's knowledge of the Law. She willingly submits to his questioning, enjoying their friendly rivalry.

"Can you tell me," he asks, "which sea creatures we Jews are permitted to eat?"

"Oh, Nathan," she answers with mock disdain, "any housewife could answer that—only those with fins and scales. It's insulting of you even to ask."

"I humbly apologize," Nathan replies with a grin. After a moment's pause, he continues, "All right, how about this one: What does the Torah teach about the washing of hands?"

"You mean the hands *specifically*, I presume?"

"Yes."

Mara pauses to reflect. "Well, I can think of several teachings. Of course, the priests must wash their hands and feet in the brass laver before they minister to the congregation or offer up the burnt sacrifice."

"True."

"And certainly one who has a bodily discharge should wash his hands before he comes in contact with anyone."

"Definitely!"

"And then if the body of a murdered man is found outside a city's walls and no one knows who has killed him, the elders of that city wash their hands to proclaim their innocence."

"Absolutely right," says Nathan. "And what about washing the hands before breaking bread?"

"It is a tradition," Mara replies, "but it is not Torah."

"Mara, you amaze me," Nathan says admiringly. "I really did expect that last question to confuse you, but …"

"So you are now convinced," Mara remarks with glee, "that a woman's mind is actually capable of absorbing Torah teachings?"

She looks up, expecting to see Nathan's unruly grin, but to her surprise, he looks quite serious. "To be truthful, Mara, I had another reason for bringing up that question. My father was recently sent to Galilee with a delegation from the Sanhedrin to investigate this Yeshua. One of the questions they asked him was why his followers were violating the very tradition you just spoke of."

"You mean by not washing their hands before breaking bread?"

"Exactly. And Yeshua had the audacity to tell them that, by some of their traditions, they were actually disobeying the Lord's commandments and that a man is defiled not by what enters his mouth, but by what comes out of it. Of course, they were stunned to hear such things from this young rabbi from nowhere—from Nazareth, of all places." Nathan hesitates, "But I cannot help wondering how he can do the things he is said to have done if he is nothing more than an upstart. That is why I simply have to see and hear him for myself."

"It seems you will not have long to wait," Mara observes. For by now they are approaching the Huldah Gates at the south end of the Temple Mount.

On the steps leading up to the gates, a crowd has gathered. A dark-haired young man is on the top step. He is seated, as teachers traditionally are. But nothing else about this gathering is at all traditional. The Pharisees and doctors of the Law that she has so often seen in these Temple precincts are generally surrounded by a group of young Torah scholars. But Yeshua is surrounded by an unlikely company consisting mostly of tradesmen, along with some beggars, a scattering of women and children, a few Pharisees, who are eyeing him warily, and two Temple guards. Though Mara and Nathan can see him, the din of the surrounding crowd prevents them, at first, from distinguishing his words.

As Nathan takes Mara's arm and edges her forward, an anxious-looking woman asks them, "Isn't this the man they seek to *kill*?"

Before either of them can answer, a young man in front of them overhears her. He spins around and remarks, "Look! He's speaking boldly right on the Temple steps. If they want to get rid of him, why do they not arrest him? Do they think he might be the Messiah?"

An older man laughs and says, "You must be joking. Shall the Messiah come out of Galilee? Must he not rather come from Bethlehem, the city of David, as the prophet Micah foretold?"

From the way some of Yeshua's listeners are looking at him, Mara is quite certain they believe that he *is* the Anointed One. More eager than ever to hear what he is saying, she and Nathan squeeze into a space near the bottom of the steps and off to one side.

Now Mara can catch most of his words: "I do nothing of myself ... My teaching is not mine ... but comes from the One that sent me."

He is interrupted by an angry outburst from one of the Pharisees: "So, who do you think you are that you should speak for HaShem Himself?"

Yeshua turns, looks directly into his eyes, and asks, "Whose teachings hold authority for *you*?"

"The teachings of Moses and the prophets," he snaps back, "not the words of some upstart preacher from Galilee."

Several voices shout in agreement. Still others call out, "Enough! Let us hear what he has to say." Mara feels caught in the crossfire, but she notices that Yeshua waits calmly for the outbursts to subside.

Then he declares in a clear, firm voice: "Moses and the prophets also spoke for Him. I have not come to dispute their teachings. I have come to *fulfill* them." With palms outstretched, he asks them, "How can I do that if not by living the Torah command to love the Lord our God with all the heart and soul and might? How can I do that if I speak on my own authority and not His? If I seek my own glory and not His? No, I tell you plainly, a man who flaunts his own knowledge, even of Torah, is but a passing shadow. But a man who bears witness to the truth that the Father reveals to him is a light to the world. If you continue in this truth I speak to you and *know* it, it will set you free."

"Set us free?" interjects another Pharisee. "Are we merely slaves, then, and not sons of Abraham?"

Unperturbed, Yeshua turns his head and looks up at him. "If you sin, you are the slaves of sin. If you were truly sons of Abraham, you would not seek to kill me. You would rejoice to see me as Abraham did."

"Nonsense," retorts the Pharisee. "You are less than fifty years old. How can you have known Abraham?"

Yeshua's brief reply almost takes Mara's breath away: "Before Abraham was, I am."

"What more do we need to hear?" says one of the Pharisees. He turns to the guards and commands, "Arrest him." But they stand rooted in place like statues. "Why do you stand there?" snaps the Pharisee. "You have an order to carry out."

Meanwhile, Yeshua has risen to his feet. He is not as tall as Mara had assumed. The guards are at least half a head taller. Yet he walks slowly past them toward the entrance gate that leads to the Temple courts. No one stops him. No one says a word. In fact, even the Pharisees are tongue-tied as they watch Yeshua disappear through the gate.

Awestruck, Mara looks up at Nathan. He takes her arm and steers her toward home.

⸎

Mara and her parents are in their rooftop sukkah, partaking of their evening meal. Up to this moment she has said nothing to them of her encounter with Yeshua that afternoon. But even though she still wants time to consider her own initial impression of him, she also yearns to hear what her father knows and thinks of him. So she finally asks, "Abba, who *is* this man Yeshua of Nazareth?"

"So, how long have you known about Yeshua, Mara?" her father inquires.

"Nathan told me about him this afternoon and took me to the Temple to hear him teach."

Mara feels her father's mood darken. "Mara, you must stay away when he is teaching. Many of the Pharisees and Sadducees are strongly opposed to him, and there could easily be trouble. Please, do not put yourself in danger."

"I do not understand their opposition," Mara insists. "He spoke only of obeying the Torah, loving HaShem, and speaking His Word."

"Mara, I am not disputing his teachings." Eleazar explains, "only trying to keep my daughter safe."

"Please, heed what your father says to you, Mara," her mother, Hannah, interjects. "Why must you be so strong-willed?"

Mara turns to her mother. "I love and respect my father, Ima. You *know* that. But today I heard a man speak with an authority rooted in something deeper than scholarship. Yet at the same time he was so meek. I cannot explain it, but it touched me deeply."' Then she looks searchingly at her father and asks, "Can you tell me why the Sanhedrin members oppose him, Abba?"

"Such a simple question should have a simple answer," he begins, "or so you young people suppose. But it is not really so simple. The simple answer would be that, because the crowds are drawn to him, he could prove to be a rabble-rouser and cause us trouble with the Romans."

"And the not-so-simple answer?" Mara probes.

Her father closes his eyes for a moment and takes a deep breath. "Having lived with me, Mara, you know that a Pharisee's life is deeply devoted to understanding and obeying the laws HaShem has given us through Moses. We work hard at it. We take it very seriously. And then there appears a young man who claims to have a direct line to Him and even backs up that claim with wondrous healing works. Has he found a better way than the one we have so long labored at? The question is unbearable, almost unthinkable. So, many of us prefer to believe him an imposter."

"Do *you*, Abba?" asks Mara, looking intently into his eyes.

"I have never seen him, and I cannot form a valid opinion solely on hearsay."

"So you will decide for yourself when you *have* seen him?"

"Exactly."

"Good," Mara responds with satisfaction. But she cannot help adding, "I do hope it will be soon."

"And *I* hope that my daughter will soon help me clean up these plates and cups," her mother announces with barely a hint of a smile.

"I expect she will, Hannah. But there is one thing to be done first," says Eleazar. After reaching for his prayer shawl, he begins to recite in his deep, resonant voice the words that are so deeply imprinted in Mara's heart and memory: *"Shema Yisrael, Adonai elohenu Adonai ehad . . ."*

3

The following week

The rooftop looks positively barren without the sukkah, but Mara has climbed up here today with some fresh figs from this year's abundant crop. At her mother's behest, she is spreading them out in the sun on straw mats to dry for use during the winter months. The sun's rays are brilliant, making the autumn day feel almost like summer.

Without the sukkah obstructing her vision, Mara has vista views in almost all directions. One in particular draws her attention. When her work is finished, she strides across to the northeastern corner of the rooftop and lays her hands on the rough cornice of its sturdy brick wall. From here she can look up and see the lofty symbols of the two immense conflicting forces in her world.

First, there is the Temple, the center of her faith, towering majestically above Mt. Zion, where it has stood, in one form or another, for some nine hundred years. Jews come from all parts of the Roman Empire to pray and offer sacrifices in its sacred precincts.

Just north of the Temple, looking almost like a constituent part of its complex, is the Antonia Fortress, headquarters of the Roman army. From its towers, Roman soldiers keep a watchful eye on all that takes place in the Temple courts.

Mara knows that the freedom her people now enjoy to worship in their Temple depends entirely upon the consent of their Roman rulers. If a riot should break out in the Temple courts, that freedom could end tomorrow. She understands her father's concern about this. He has told her about the occasion, back when he was a boy, when the Romans had stripped their council, the Sanhedrin, of much of its civic authority, giving it the final say only in religious matters. A misstep on the part of any of the Jews could lead to further losses of freedom. Regrettably, the fortress rules the Temple. And like so many of her people, Mara longs for the day when their Messiah will come and free them from the domination of these idol-worshipers from Rome.

Hearing heavy footsteps scuffing their way up the stairs to the rooftop, Mara turns to see her father emerging from below. His usually calm face is flushed, and he is breathing heavily.

"Mara," he begins, before he has quite reached the rooftop, "I have made an interesting discovery at the Temple today."

"And you have come all the way up here to tell me about it, Abba?" she asks with a smile. "It must be well worth hearing!"

"I am quite certain you will find it so." Eleazar catches his breath and continues, "Have you ever encountered someone in an unaccustomed place? He may look familiar, but at first you simply cannot recall where he fits into the context of your life."

"I know just what you mean" she responds. "Did you encounter someone at the Temple today?"

"Yes, a cripple named Tobias," her father replies. "I have seen him many times over the years, lying on his mat near the Pool of Bethesda. He always stayed near the pool because, as you probably know, the first person who gets into it after its waters move is supposed to find healing. You have seen how many sick people cluster around that pool. It takes quick action to be the first one in. Since he could hardly move, he could *never* be the first. I felt so sorry for him that sometimes I would hand him a coin or offer him a drink of water."

"And he was at the Temple today?"

"Yes, at the morning sacrifice."

"I wonder how he got there."

"Well, that is the remarkable thing," Eleazar explains. "He got there on his own two feet. So besides seeing him away from the pool, I was also seeing him standing upright—a most unexpected sight."

"So, how did he come to be walking today?"

"That is what I have come to tell you about," he responds, smiling down at her. "Tobias said that one day—it was during the *Shavuot* Festival last year—a man came over to him and commanded him, with an authority that was not to be denied, to take up his mat and walk. Tobias told me he has been walking freely ever since."

"Now I know why you are telling me this!" Mara exclaims. "The man must have been Yeshua."

"Indeed he was."

"So, what do you make of it, Abba?" she inquires eagerly. "Can you really believe him an imposter after hearing this?"

"The more I know of him, the more difficult it becomes." Eleazar pauses. "But how can I be certain until I have heard him for myself?"

"When will that be?" she asks, hoping to veil her eagerness.

"Well, he usually comes here for the festivals," her father reflects. "We will soon be celebrating *Hanukkah*. Perhaps then he will teach in the Temple again ... if the Sanhedrin does not arrest him first."

"If he *is* teaching then, will you go to hear him, Abba?"

"Yes, I will," he replies, answering just as she was hoping he would.

She gives an inaudible sigh of relief and asks, hoping even more fervently, "And if and when you go to hear him, will you promise to take me with you?"

He looks down at her uneasily. "Mara, you know the danger ..."

"How could I be in danger if *you* were with me, Abba?" she asks, attempting to reason with him.

He hesitates and finally answers, "All right, Daughter, I will consider your request, but I cannot make you a promise. You would not wish to use a promise as a tool to divert me from the exercise of my best judgment, would you, Mara?'"

"I suppose not, Abba," she replies ... without one jot of conviction.

4

Two months later, the Feast of Hanukkah

When the week of the festival finally arrives, Eleazar does not disappoint Mara. Though the day is cool, breezy, and overcast, he tells her he is going to the Temple, where, he has heard, Yeshua is teaching. Best of all, he invites Mara to join him. She winds her woolen shawl around her head and shoulders as they step into the street.

As Mara and her father thread their way through the crowd in the direction of the Temple, he turns to her and says, "Mara, please understand that under no circumstances are you to leave my side. Your mother thinks I am out of my mind to take you to the Temple at festival time, and if anything should happen to you ..."

"Nothing will, Abba," Mara assures him. "I will be right beside you, and not only for my safety. I want to know your opinion of Yeshua."

"So do I," her father responds with a mysterious trace of a grin.

Today there is no sign of Yeshua on the steps where Mara had heard him teaching at Sukkot. Eleazar takes her arm and leads her to the Huldah entrance gate, through which she had seen the young rabbi disappear on that occasion. Swiftly they ascend the ramp beyond it to the outer court of the Temple.

This court is known as the Court of the Gentiles because it is the only part of the Temple precincts where non-Jews are admitted. Especially at festival seasons, it is a gigantic swirl of motion and sounds and scents. Vendors are selling doves and livestock for sacrifices, and tables have been set up where people can exchange their foreign currency for a Jewish half-shekel, the amount required for the annual Temple tax. Edging the court is Solomon's Portico, a long colonnade where Pharisees and doctors of the Law often meet with their pupils, sheltered and somewhat removed from the noise. Towering above the tumult of the court is the serene majesty of the Temple, still under construction since the time of Herod the Great, but nonetheless magnificent with its soaring gilded columns.

Mara wonders at first how they will ever find Yeshua in this swarm of people until she catches sight of an unusually large gathering at the far corner of Solomon's Portico—a cluster of people that includes a number of women. She points it out to her father and suggests they look for him there.

As they draw closer, Mara notices that there are Pharisees in the group as well. Eleazar is surprised to discover that one of them is his friend and colleague Joseph, a rabbi from Arimathaea, who, like himself, is a member of the Sanhedrin. As Mara suspected, Yeshua is indeed seated in the midst of this gathering, and as they draw closer, they hear one of the Pharisees insistently questioning him.

"How long are you going to keep us in doubt?" he probes. "If you *are* the Christ, just tell us so."

"I *have* told you," Yeshua responds, "but you have chosen not to believe me. The works that I do in my Father's name — they bear witness of who I am, and they give living proof that His kingdom is indeed here among you."

"Show us this kingdom then," shouts another of the Pharisees. "Where are we to find it?"

Yeshua looks around him into the eyes of his listeners before answering. "You will not find it by searching around for it. You will not be able to say, 'Oh, here it is,' or 'There it is.' Like leaven, it is at work—hidden from sight, yet transforming all it touches. To see it, you will need to look again with new eyes, for His kingdom is *within* you. My followers know this, and because they do, they shall never perish nor can they be snatched out of my Father's hand." He pauses for a moment and then reaches out his open palms. "All that I do is the work of my Father—the sign of His kingdom within me. I do nothing of myself. I and my Father are one."

At this point several of the Pharisees pick up stones to hurl at him—all of them, as far as Mara can see, except Joseph and Eleazar. Mara feels her father's hand tighten around her wrist as he tugs her back from the center of the crowd.

Yeshua turns to his would-be attackers and says, "I have shown you many of my Father's good works. For which of them are you stoning me? Perhaps for the man born blind who received his sight at Sukkot?"

One of them answers, "Nonsense. We do not stone you for a good work, but for blasphemy. You, a mere man, are making yourself out to be God."

"Do the Scriptures err then," Yeshua asks them, "in saying 'all of you are children of the Most High'? You fault the Scriptures if you call it blasphemy for me to say 'I am the Son of God.' The Father sent me to do His work. Do not believe me unless I carry it out. But if I do, believe what the *works* tell you even if you cannot believe *me*. Then you will know that I am in the Father, and the Father in me."

By this time most of the Pharisees have dropped their stones. As they well know, a stoning in the Temple court at festival time would bring swift retribution from the Roman soldiers in the fortress, but a few of them move closer in an attempt to seize Yeshua. To reach him, they must circle around several of his followers, rugged-looking fishermen from Galilee. By the time they reach the place where Yeshua was sitting, he has disappeared into the crowd.

While he was addressing them, Mara had noticed a woman standing near him—just to his right. The woman's eyes had been fixed on him every moment he was speaking. Now Mara is yearning to talk to her, to find out what *she* knows of Yeshua. When Mara asks Eleazar's permission, the anxious look in his eyes tells her exactly how he would *like* to answer. But still he says to her, "Perhaps for a moment, Mara, but, as you know, it would be improper for me to approach a stranger who is a woman. You will have to speak with her alone. But I will be standing close behind you, and when I speak your name, you must leave with me immediately."

Mara, of course, agrees. As she draws closer to the woman, however, she finds herself groping blindly for something to say to her. She can scarcely imagine how to begin a conversation about the man who has just left the air ringing with his extraordinary words. But the woman sees her approaching and

and bridges the awkward distance between them with a gentle smile.

"Is this the first time you have heard Yeshua teach?" she asks with a trace of a Galilean accent.

"No," Mara replies haltingly. "I heard him on the south steps during Sukkot." Then she brings herself to ask, "Are you one of his followers?"

"Yes," she answers, "I most certainly am. Quite a number of us have journeyed here with him from Galilee for the festival."

"Does he have many women followers?" Mara inquires.

"More than you might suppose. He does not treat us as most men do. To him we are as worthy as they are."

"Is that why you follow him?"

"No, that is only a small part of it," the woman replies. After a moment's reflection, she continues, "What draws me to Yeshua is that he does not simply *speak* of the Father. He makes Him visible. To me, Yeshua is ... His pure shining."

"What makes you so certain of that?" Mara probes.

"It is as he said," she answers. "His works speak for him. I, of all people, know this. He has given me back my life."

"How?" Mara asks, marveling at the forcefulness of this stranger's assertion.

"When I was a young girl no older than you," she explains, "a horrible seizure came upon me like an attack of demons. It threw me to the ground and left me helpless—unable to move or speak. For years these seizures would come upon me without warning. I lived in constant dread of them until one day Yeshua came to my village—to Magdala. He commanded those demons to depart from me, and they have never returned. Even the *fear* of them has left me. He restored my life that day."

"Mara!" Her father's deep voice summons her back to the present moment.

"I must go now," she tells the woman from Magdala.

"So your name is Mara," she says. "Mine is Mary." And she clasps Mara's hand in a warm gesture of farewell.

Eleazar says not a word to Mara as they cross the Court of the Gentiles and descend the ramp to the exit gate. When they finally emerge onto the street, she can wait no longer.

"So, what is your opinion of Yeshua, Abba?" she asks. "Do you think him an imposter?"

"The word *imposter* certainly does not describe him," answers Eleazar, "though exactly what word *does* characterize him is quite beyond my powers of description."

"The Pharisees asked him if he was Christ—the Messiah. Do you think he may be?"

"That is a difficult question to answer, Mara," he replies, "as the Pharisees well knew when they used it to bait him. Even in my lifetime there have been some who were *thought* to be the Messiah. When I was not much older than you are, a man named Theudas, whom I found rather boastful, proclaimed himself a prophet and had a following of some four hundred men. But he was killed, and his followers disbanded, and it all came to nothing."

"But Yeshua is not like that," Mara insists. "He never seeks glory for himself."

"I can see that, Mara," her father assures her. "Everything he says and does seems to be for the Lord alone. But this young carpenter from Galilee certainly does not resemble the great warrior-king we have so long been *expecting* as our Messiah. In the time of Quirinius, Judas of Galilee convinced many that it was he. He boldly led a rebellion against the Romans, but then he, too, came to a bad end."

"I cannot imagine Yeshua wielding a sword," Mara observes, "but somehow he seems mightier than those who do. He healed Mary, the woman I spoke with, of fearful demonic seizures."

"I am not surprised, then, that she appears to be such a devoted follower of his," Eleazar remarks. "I believe my friend Joseph is also one of his followers, but being a member of the Sanhedrin, he obviously cannot acknowledge that publicly."

"Can Yeshua's friends in the Sanhedrin protect him from those who seek to kill him?"

Eleazar pauses. "That is unlikely, Mara. The high priest, Caiaphas, is most antagonistic to him, and those who approve of him are a tiny minority who would put themselves in grave danger by supporting him openly."

"So there is nothing you can do to safeguard him?"

"Nothing that I can see." He pauses. Then, with a suddenness that startles her, he turns to her and asks, "Tell me, Mara. Do you consider *yourself* one of his followers?"

"Sometimes I ask myself that," she answers hesitantly.

"O, my dear Daughter, please be careful," he entreats her as they cross the threshold of their still peaceful home.

5

The following winter

The winter months have brought no further Temple visits from Yeshua, but in spite of this, they have been far from uneventful.

Rachel has sent word from Jericho that she and Matthias are expecting their first child in early summer. Mara tries to write to her sister, but the words stubbornly refuse to form themselves. Rachel might as well be living in a different world. This deep divide saddens Mara because she truly loves her sister. She recalls the night, a week or so before Rachel's wedding, when the two sisters had lain side by side on their sleeping mats and talked deep into the night of their hopes and dreams. Rachel had encouraged Mara to pursue her studies even though her own dreams centered on marriage and motherhood. Now, less than a year later, Rachel's first child is already on the way. Mara can hardly imagine herself an aunt, let alone a mother.

But only yesterday she received an unwelcome reminder that motherhood is exactly what is expected of her sooner or later. Mara received her first proposal of marriage. It came from a young man named Reuben who had studied Torah with her father back when Mara was just a little girl. She had not seen him for several years, but when he came back to visit Eleazar, Mara noticed that he was looking at her in quite a different way —as if she were a piece of ripe fruit he wanted to bite into. It made her very uneasy. When Eleazar broke the news that Reuben had asked him for her hand in marriage, Mara dissolved into tears. But her father was as merciful to her as he had been to Rachel. He told Reuben that Mara was still too young for marriage and that he must wait at least two years before renewing his suit. Mara hopes that by that time he will have found himself another bride.

Now, as she and her mother are preparing the evening meal, Ima turns to her and says, "I do not understand you, Mara. A fine young man—devoted to HaShem, well provided for, even handsome—asks for your hand, and you cry like a baby. What were you thinking of?"

Mara stares down at the melon she is slicing. "How can I explain it to you, Ima? I did not like the way Reuben was looking at me. I felt as if being married to him would use me up and leave nothing but a ... a rind," she says, holding up a slice of the melon.

"So, what man does *not* look at a pretty woman that way, Mara?" her mother asks. "Perhaps you are expecting too much. Do you think an angel of the Lord will come and claim you as his bride?"

"Of course not, Ima," Mara answers. Then, searching her mother's eyes, she adds, "But when Abba asked for *your* hand, I am certain he cared about more than just your looks."

"Not even those, Mara," Ima responds. "In fact, I did not meet your father until the day of our wedding."

Mara gasps. "How frightened you must have been!"

"I was a little nervous perhaps, but not frightened," Hannah recalls. "My father, who loved me, had chosen this man for my husband. I knew he would choose wisely, and he did. You can be certain that your father will do the same."

"I am grateful that my father is not one to force a daughter into an unhappy marriage. Remember, Ima, he turned down two proposals for Rachel before Matthias asked for her hand."

"Your father is a man of exceptional patience, Mara," her mother acknowledges. "But do not try his patience too far."

Mara's concerns about marriage and motherhood are soon eclipsed by the news she hears from Nathan several days later. He comes bolting through the door of her house in breathless excitement, eager to reveal the story he has just heard from at least ten different people on his way home from the marketplace.

"I don't see how it can be true," he forewarns her, "but I heard exactly the same story from all of them."

"So *tell* it," she prods him. "Are you trying to see how long you can keep me in suspense?"

"No, Mara," he answers, somewhat stung by her question. "But something has happened that is ... well ... simply impossible. Only it cannot be because it really happened. At least everyone says it did."

Mara has never heard Nathan sound so incoherent. "Perhaps if you will tell me," she urges him, "we can decide that together."

"All right," he says, taking a deep breath. "You know Yeshua has not been seen in Jerusalem for a long time."

"Yes, at least two months. Is he coming back here?"

"Perhaps. All I know is that he was in Bethany this morning."

"Bethany!" Mara exclaims. "That is an easy walk from here. He *must* be coming to Jerusalem."

"I would not count on it, Mara," Nathan advises her. "But what he did in Bethany today has spread to Jerusalem even *without* his presence here."

"What was it?"

"Well, he came to Bethany because his friend Lazarus was very ill. But by the time he arrived there, Lazarus was already dead. In fact, he had been in his grave for four days."

"Too long, then, for his spirit to return to him," observes Mara.

"So we have always believed. But, nevertheless, Yeshua stood outside the tomb and called to Lazarus, ordering him to come out." Nathan pauses and looks searchingly at Mara. "How many of the people in the crowd outside that tomb do you think actually believed he would do it?"

"Not many. Would *you* have?"

"Probably not," Nathan admits. "But he *did* come out, or so I have been told. He could hardly walk with the grave clothes wound around him, but somehow he managed to come out— very much alive."

Mara is silent for a long moment. Then she turns to him and says, "I believe it, Nathan. I do not think I would have believed it before hearing Yeshua teach, but I can believe it now."

"Why?" he asks.

"Because of what Yeshua told us that day in the Temple court," Mara replies. "He does not bring about these wonders through his own abilities. It is his Father at work in him. It is the Almighty."

"Then why does He not work such miracles through you and me?" Nathan wonders aloud.

"Perhaps He would," Mara observes, "if we were as willing as Yeshua is to be nothing but His shining."

"You may be right, Mara," Nathan agrees. "But it is certainly not easy to be as willing as Yeshua is. What do you think makes it so difficult?"

Mara weighs his question. "The self, I think. I doubt that I could have made myself submit willingly to marrying Reuben even if I had thought it was the will of HaShem Himself."

"Perhaps it was not," Nathan suggests.

"You may be right, but that is not the question. The truth is that I would not be willing even if it were." Mara smiles up at him and confides, "My mother calls me strong-willed."

"Is that such a bad thing?" Nathan asks encouragingly.

"In a woman it is generally considered to be, as I am certain you have noticed," Mara replies. "In any case, it will surely disqualify me from raising the dead any time in the near future."

6

A week later

As it turns out, Mara's hopes that Yeshua will journey from Bethany to Jerusalem are not to be fulfilled, but knowing that he will almost certainly be there for Passover makes the weeks of waiting easier to endure. What she finds almost beyond endurance, however, is an occasion when her female role cuts her off—temporarily, at least—from what is being said about him.

Two of Eleazar's friends, fellow Pharisees and members of the Sanhedrin, are visiting him at home. One of them she recognizes as Joseph, the man her father had pointed out to her in the crowd at the Temple during the Hanukkah festival. She remembers that he is a secret follower of Yeshua. The other man she does not recognize, but she surmises that he, too, may be one of Yeshua's followers because of the brief, enticing snatches of conversation that reach her in the kitchen area of the house.

Yes, that is where Mara must stay on this memorable occasion when, if she had been Eleazar's *son*, she might have been reclining at dinner with him and his colleagues instead of assisting her mother in preparing the meal. Since Hannah, who has little or no interest in their discussion, has taken it upon herself to serve, Mara has no excuse to enter the room where they are dining even for a minute or two at a time. She is certain that, if only she could, she would be able to hear enough of the conversation to piece it together.

At one point, while Hannah is serving, Mara moves closer to the doorway. Although she is dutifully occupied in drying a bowl, her mother scolds her when she catches her there.

"Keep to your place, Mara," she says—somewhat sharply, Mara feels. "What they are discussing is *men's* business."

"But, Ima, it concerns Yeshua."

"I know that, Mara. You would do well to keep your distance from Yeshua," her mother warns her. "I do not say he is evil. He may be a very good man for all I know. But he could cause us a great deal of trouble."

Mara feels the too familiar anger welling up. If only she could be at peace—experience the Father's kingdom within her, as Yeshua had expressed it. And the irony is that what is destroying her peace right now is her inability to hear what these men are saying about *him*. For all she knows, they may be discussing his teachings about the kingdom at this very moment.

Not until the visitors have left and the last platter has been shelved does she finally get to hear her father's report of the evening. When they are alone together at last, she learns that the second visitor's name is Nicodemus. During the Passover festival several years earlier, he had sought out Yeshua on the Mount of Olives just east of the city, where he often takes refuge. Nicodemus had guessed correctly—Yeshua was there, alone.

"What did Nicodemus say to him when he finally found him?" Mara inquires.

"He told Yeshua that his miracles were ample proof that the Lord was with him and had sent him," Eleazar replies.

"And what did Yeshua say to that?" asks Mara, trying to coax the story out of him.

"That is what Nicodemus has been trying to understand ever since. Yeshua told him that unless a man is born again he cannot see the Lord's kingdom."

"Born again!" Mara exclaims. "Whatever did he mean by that?"

"Well, he certainly was not suggesting the possibility of re-emerging from the womb," her father assures her. "He spoke of being born of the *Spirit*."

"I wonder how that comes about."

"So did Nicodemus. And then Yeshua pointed out that a spiritual leader of Israel should *know* such things—things to which he and his followers had openly borne witness." Eleazar pauses. "Nicodemus told us that Yeshua left him very much humbled ... and with a great deal to ponder."

"Yes, I can imagine," Mara remarks. Then she asks, "Has he become one of Yeshua's followers?"

"Not openly because of his position on the Sanhedrin," her father reminds her. "But he greatly respects him and tries to follow his teachings."

"Is that why he wanted to meet with you and Joseph?"

"Yes," Eleazar replies. "Because of the need for secrecy, he had not dared to seek out other followers of Yeshua among his acquaintances. Then recently he somehow learned of Joseph's interest in Yeshua, and Joseph assured him that I was no danger to them. He is grateful to have friends with whom he can speak freely of Yeshua without fear that his secret will be betrayed to Caiaphas and the others."

"So you are 'no danger'? Does that mean you are also a follower of Yeshua?" Mara asks hopefully.

"No, Mara," her father answers, "but that does not prevent me from being in sympathy with some who are his followers."

"Is that sympathy just because of me?"

"Not entirely," he assures her. "Having heard Yeshua speak, I must admit that I respect him. In fact, I am somewhat in awe of him. Never have I seen a man so ... so aglow with the Spirit of the Lord. But I am also conscious of the dangers that he, with his influential presence in Jerusalem, could bring raining down upon us Jews. Imagine what could happen if he or his followers were to antagonize the Romans! And after what occurred in Bethany only a week ago, his influence here could be beyond our imagining."

"Could that miracle in Bethany be a sign to us that he actually *is* our Messiah?" Mara wonders aloud. "Perhaps he is the Anointed One destined to free us from the tyranny of Rome."

"You are certainly not the first to consider that possibility, Mara," her father answers. "But if he is, it will take a miracle beyond any that he has worked thus far."

7

Early spring, several days before Passover

If ever a day was designed for a miracle, Mara reflects, surely it is today. The sky is cloudless, and the sun beams down like the face of HaShem Himself.

Her people are about to celebrate Passover, a holiday especially close to their hearts. For over a thousand years, it has commemorated the day when Moses, following a progression of ten miracles, finally won their ancestors' freedom from slavery in Egypt. Every year, thousands of Jews converge in Jerusalem from every corner of the Roman Empire to celebrate this all-important event. This year, too, as on every Passover Mara can remember, they fill every inn and cover the hillsides surrounding the city with their tents.

What sets *this* Passover apart, however, is the hope that fills the hearts of so many of these pilgrims. Two months ago, a man had commanded his friend Lazarus, four days dead, to come out from the rock-cut tomb where he was buried, and he had come out—alive. The man who could work such a miracle as that—might he not be the Moses of *their* time, their Messiah, their liberator from the Roman yoke? In any case, the resurrection at Bethany ensures that the name Yeshua will be on everyone's lips, whether or not they believe he is—or might be—their Messiah.

Word has it that he has spent the Sabbath in Bethany with Lazarus and his sisters and that he will be arriving in Jerusalem this very day. Mara has waited four months for his return. The fact that it coincides with the Passover holiday is not lost on her. He comes to bring liberation as Moses did. She is certain of that. And nothing anyone can say could keep her away from the crowds who will be craning their necks for a glimpse of him.

Her father, Eleazar, will not be able to accompany her, however. He was called early this morning to an emergency meeting of the Sanhedrin. This does not surprise Mara. No prophetic gift is required to see the threat of a possible conflict looming. At the same time that Yeshua is approaching Jerusalem from the east, the Roman governor, Pontius Pilatus, will be entering the city from the west, coming from his headquarters in Caesarea. He will be arriving in imperial splendor, surrounded by soldiers mounted on horseback. With the largest Passover crowds in anyone's memory engulfing the city, a disastrous confrontation must be prevented at all costs, and the Sanhedrin is determined to see that it is.

Since her father is otherwise occupied, Mara goes to Nathan's door in search of a companion for today's adventure. They soon find themselves in a surging current of humanity, most of it flowing east toward the Kidron Valley and the Mount of Olives. Around them they hear snatches of conversation, some of it in languages they do not even recognize, let alone understand.

Mara does her best, however, to reply to a stout, gray-haired woman, who asks her in Greek, which Mara speaks haltingly, "Have you ever seen this Yeshua?"

"Yes, twice," she answers. "He sometimes comes here for the festivals."

"Then surely you must have seen him work at least one of his miracles," the woman states inquisitively.

"No," Mara replies, "but I have *heard* about one of them from a woman he healed."

"Well, after coming all the way from Antioch, I will be very disappointed if he does not work at least one miracle today," she comments just before her husband seizes her arm and sweeps her off into the crowd.

Mara turns to Nathan with a droll expression on her face. "She speaks of Yeshua as if he were a street magician," she observes.

"In a crowd this size, Mara, you are likely to discover hundreds of different views of him," he remarks with a smile. Then he asks her, "What do *you* expect of him?"

"I don't know what to expect, Nathan. I simply hope."

"You hope he is the Messiah?"

"Yes, the true King of the Jews."

"And what claim does a carpenter from Nazareth have to that title?"

"More claim than Herod the Great, an Edomite appointed by the Roman senate," Mara insists. "At least Yeshua is actually a Jew, and I hear he is of the tribe of Judah, just as King David was."

"You argue forcefully, Mara, but somehow I doubt that your hopes rest mainly on his pedigree," Nathan teases.

"You are most observant, Nathan," she replies facetiously. Then she adds, after a moment's reflection, "But I am not certain that my hopes rest solely on his wondrous works either. What speaks loudest to me is the authority he wields with such meekness. I have never experienced anything like it."

By now Mara and Nathan can see the Kidron Valley stretching before them. It is already swarming with people. Some of them are carrying palm branches in their hands, preparing to greet Yeshua in a manner suited to a king. The crowds are most thickly concentrated along the road that winds in a northwesterly direction down the Mount of Olives and then cuts across the valley toward the city walls. They both agree that to cross the valley and try to find a place to stand anywhere near the road would be fruitless. From where they are now, partway up the Temple Mount, they can see some stretches of the road Yeshua will travel. If they stay where they are, close to the road on the west side of the valley, he will surely pass near them on his way to the Temple.

They wait. The sun moves westward, and the crowds swell. Just when it seems they can endure no more waiting, Mara and Nathan begin to hear distant shouts from the crest of the Mount of Olives. Palm branches are being waved in the air as the crowd gravitates as one body toward a figure Mara can barely distinguish. She has no doubt, however, that it is Yeshua. The wave of excitement builds as he slowly, steadily, descends the hill.

By the time he completes the descent and begins to cross the Kidron Valley, they can see that he is not walking but riding on a donkey's colt just big enough to bear his weight. Mara remembers the words of the prophet Zechariah: "Shout, O daughter of Jerusalem. Behold, your King comes to you, lowly, and riding on the colt of a donkey." She feels as if she is living, in this very moment, the fulfillment of that prophecy.

And she knows that she is not alone in this feeling. Some in the crowd are placing palm branches and even their outer clothing in Yeshua's path so that the dust will not soil the garments of their King. At last she can hear what they are shouting—words from a psalm that she knows by heart: "Hosanna to the son of David. Blessed is the King who comes in the name of the Lord."

Mara's heart beats faster as the tiny donkey with its precious burden draws closer and closer. She hears two of the Pharisees conversing right behind her. They have evidently heard the shouting and come down from the Temple to see what is happening. One of them comments bitterly, "Do you see what all our efforts have come to? It seems as if the whole world is following after this man."

At last Yeshua comes into full view, lurching along on top of his humble little mount. Clothes and palm branches are quickly spread out on the dusty road before him. The voices cry out ever louder the closer he gets.

Suddenly, one of the Pharisees behind Mara shouts to Yeshua in a harsh twang that pierces the enthusiastic clamor of the crowd, "Rabbi, you are approaching the Temple. Speak to these followers of yours and bid them be quiet."

The procession comes to a dead stop directly in front of Mara and Nathan. Yeshua turns to the Pharisee who has just shouted the command. "I tell you," he replies, "that even if these people were silenced, the very stones on the roadside would cry out." Then he continues his ascent toward the Temple.

Mara notices that Yeshua's face is particularly solemn today. His mood seems strangely at odds with the exuberance of the multitude of hopeful Jews who are celebrating his arrival. What is on his mind? she wonders. What does he know that the rest of us do not?

When Mara comes bounding excitedly through the door of her house later that afternoon, her celebratory mood is abruptly extinguished. Although it is not the usual hour for it, she finds her father wearing his prayer shawl and *tefillin*, standing and swaying in an attitude of prayer. She waits respectfully while he finishes, but her heart is beating impatiently.

When he finally turns his face toward her, however, his expression is so somber that the words she was about to say die on her lips, and she never gets to describe to him the wonder she has just witnessed. Instead she hears herself asking him, "Abba, why do you look so sad?"

"Oh, Mara," he says, eyes downcast. "Our council has made a grievous decision today. I do not even wish to speak to you of it, but you will hear of it soon enough even if I do not."

"A decision? About Yeshua?"

"Yes. Caiaphas, the high priest, told them—us—today that it is better for one man to die than for the wrath of Rome to fall on all our people."

"And Yeshua is to be that man?"

"Yes."

"How can they possibly bring about his death?" Mara asks in disbelief. "Our people will not stand for it. You should have seen the crowds celebrating him today."

"Well, as you know, the Sanhedrin no longer has the authority to pronounce a death sentence. All they can do is turn him over to Roman jurisdiction."

"On what charge?"

"Treason. His entry into Jerusalem today could easily be viewed as a claim to kingship, setting himself up as a rival to the Emperor Tiberius—to Caesar himself."

"That is absurd," Mara snaps back at him in utter disgust.

"Yes, Mara, I know."

"Didn't anyone tell them so?"

"Not in so many words, but some of us, myself included, voted against making such a charge." He hesitates before adding, "We were overwhelmingly outnumbered."

"Abba, what will they do to him?"

"If it is left to the Romans, he will probably be sentenced to the cross."

Mara gasps. "That is the most horrible death imaginable. Is there no way he can be spared?"

"Not unless he disappears from Jerusalem during the festival."

"Will he be given any choice—any warning?" Mara asks, her eyes filling with tears.

"I fear he will not," her father answers sadly. "Mara, please understand that none of this is as I would wish it to be."

"So we stand by helplessly while the best man we have ever known dies a miserable death? I hate this, Abba. I just hate it!" Mara runs from the room and climbs to the rooftop, where she huddles in one corner—a tiny, feeble, sobbing knot.

8

The following day

Mara has been unable to sleep. The thought of this meek, strong, godly man being executed by the Romans—in the excruciating and shameful manner in which they do it—is more than she can bear. On several occasions she has seen crosses outside the city walls, and even though she has tried to avert her eyes, she could not avoid hearing the anguished moans of the men who were slowly, painfully, dying on them.

If only Yeshua could go back to Ephraim, where he had been living quietly all the while that Jerusalem was abuzz with the news of Lazarus's resurrection. Mara is certain the Sanhedrin would leave him alone if their concerns about his influence on the Passover crowds could be laid to rest.

But as she soon learns, the Sanhedrin's concerns have only been heightened by today's events. During the afternoon, Nathan stops by, his face uncharacteristically grave.

He swallows hard and tells her, "Yeshua was at the Temple again today."

"What happened?" she asks. "Did they arrest him?"

"No, Mara. But he did something that may well lead to his arrest," Nathan replies, shaking his head dejectedly. "He overturned the tables of the moneychangers right in the midst of the Passover crowds. And then he stayed there, healing people— blind people, lame people—right there in the Temple courts."

"And they did not arrest him?"

"No, it would have been foolhardy to do that in such a public place. As you know, he has hundreds, maybe thousands, of supporters. It could cause a riot. But I fear it is only a question of time—a short time, at that—until they do. It could even happen tonight if they know where to find him."

"I pray no one tells them," Mara says with a shudder.

"I understand how you feel, Mara," Nathan responds, "but think of these men—the Sanhedrin, including our own fathers— trying to maintain order during this festival. This is the largest crowd Jerusalem has seen in anyone's memory. If they get out of control and the Romans have to step in, you may be certain that blood will be spilled and that more of our freedoms will be lost. No one wants that to happen." He pauses and then blurts out the words he has been holding back: "It is difficult for me to understand why Yeshua chose this occasion to overturn the moneychangers' tables. It almost seems as if he is daring the Sanhedrin to arrest him."

"Have you noticed where the moneychangers set up those tables—right in front of the entrance to the holy places of worship?" Mara rejoins. "Perhaps the Sanhedrin should have seen to it that they find a more appropriate place to carry on their business. Then there would be no need for Yeshua to protest."

"I see that you are convinced he can do no wrong. I will not argue with you," Nathan says resignedly, quietly taking his leave.

Mara has never felt more alone. Nathan has just explained with perfect logic why Yeshua must be stopped, and she is quite certain that her father would agree. The two on whom she most relies cannot be counted on to help her in the daunting task she is convinced must be done. Yeshua must be warned, not tomorrow but today. She will have to undertake it alone. Not a moment must be lost.

Mara snatches her mother's dark blue veil off the stool in the corner and swiftly drapes it around her head and shoulders, hoping that it may make her appear somewhat older than she is. Then she disappears out the door without a word to either of her parents.

She is almost certain that Yeshua will be spending the night either back in Bethany or somewhere on the Mount of Olives. If she is to find him, she must wait along the road he traveled yesterday.

Mara's sense of urgency is thwarted as she tries to elbow her way through the Passover crowds blocking her at every turn. It takes much longer than usual to reach the spot overlooking the Kidron Valley where she and Nathan had waited the previous day. But now that day seems to her like some far-off, wishful dream. *Then* Yeshua was Jerusalem's hero. Today he is a hunted man. To be as certain as possible of seeing him, she must cross to the eastern side of the valley, where the crowds are less dense and where she will be closer to his destination.

Today there are no palm branches on the valley road to keep down the dust. And the towering shapes of the rock-cut tombs that border the dusty road loom above her like a curse. Passover pilgrims trudge along the road, each one centered on his own objective. No longer are they united in a single great hope as they were yesterday.

At last she reaches the foot of the Mount of Olives. She sees an ancient, spreading olive tree several paces back from the road —its gnarled trunk offering her a welcome place to lean, its silvery green leaves fluttering in the light spring breeze. There, with pounding heart, she stations herself to watch for Yeshua.

Time passes. Clusters of men, women, and children advance along the road in both directions, most of them deep in conversation, never even looking in Mara's direction. A few glance over at her, but all of them are strangers. Even if they were not, they probably would not recognize her with her mother's dark veil covering the lower half of her face.

The sun has sunk behind the walls of the Temple, and the valley is in shadow. After her sleepless night, Mara has to summon all her strength just to keep her eyes open. She must search the face of every man who passes heading east because it *could* be Yeshua, and he must not get past her without hearing her warning.

It is barely light enough for her to distinguish faces any longer when he finally appears, walking in the midst of a small group of his followers. They seem to be absorbed in an animated exchange, and Mara suddenly realizes how unsuitable it would be for her, a young woman, to break into such a group of men. But unless she does, how can she possibly attract Yeshua's attention, let alone speak with him confidentially?

Before she has time to plan her approach, however, it dawns on Mara that he is looking directly at her, almost as if he had been expecting to meet her there. In seconds he has broken away from his followers and is standing beside her. Her heart pounding, she gazes at his sandals, unable at first to look up into his face. Then she hears him say gently, "What troubles you, Daughter?"

Somewhat shakily, she pours out the speech she has been rehearsing in her mind: the Sanhedrin's plan to charge him with treason and turn him over to the Romans, the safety awaiting him if he will only stay quietly outside Jerusalem for a time.

When her words have at last spilled out, he is silent for a moment, and his response, when it comes, takes her completely by surprise. "So you would have me retreat?" he asks her.

She hardly knows how to answer. Eventually she stammers out, "I am so afraid of what they will do to you."

When she finally dares to look up into his face, he is smiling at her tenderly. "Do you truly believe that these men have the power to defeat my Father's purpose?"

Feeling very foolish and very young, she shakes her head.

"What is your name?" he asks her.

"Mara."

"Mara, you have shown great love in coming here. This I will always remember. But you need have no fear. My Father— our Father—is wholly in charge." And then, as suddenly as he appeared, he is gone.

He is gone, but his words still echo in the air around her. *You have shown great love.* She feels as if he has lifted her to the light and seen in her something of worth—something holy. She had come here, or so she thought, to do something for *him*— something that, perhaps, she should have known he had no need of. Yet he had seen beyond her needless warning to the pure gift of love she was offering. Could not such seeing as his be the greatest gift of all and the truest form of love?

Mara wishes she could stand right here, just letting his words resound in her heart. But by now the sky is growing dark, and she must cross the Kidron Valley in order to get home. Somehow home now seems much farther away than the distance she traveled to get here. Hugging her mother's veil closely around her and keeping her eyes fixed on the ground, she concentrates all her efforts on placing one foot in front of the other on the dusty road. From time to time she hears the voices of Passover pilgrims on their way to or from their tents on the hillside. But as she nears the rock-cut tombs, a deep silence surrounds her.

In that silence, she becomes aware of heavy, unsteady footsteps approaching her from behind. She tries to move faster, but so do the menacing steps. Suddenly, she feels a rough hand clenching her shoulder, wrenching her around. Turning, she finds herself looking up into the leering face of a Roman soldier.

He snatches off her veil. She can smell the wine on his breath as he rasps out in Greek, "It is time you had a Roman warrior for a boyfriend, little Jewish wench."

She knows she is no match for his strength even in his present drunken state, but she struggles nevertheless—struggles until she loses her balance and falls, striking her head against a rock.

At once the horrifying scene fades into oblivion.

9

The following morning, before sunrise

By the time Mara regains consciousness, the scene has so completely shifted that at first she has no idea where she is. All she knows is that she is indoors, lying on a sleeping mat that rests on a ledge along the wall of a room. Through her half-closed eyes, she glimpses an oil lamp flickering nearby. Except for the painful pounding in her head, the incident with the drunken soldier would seem like nothing more than a nightmare from which she has just awakened.

She hears someone stirring and becomes aware of her mother kneeling on the floor beside her. Ima takes her hand, and for a long moment, no words pass between them. Then Mara feels a drop splash onto her hand and realizes that her mother is weeping. At first she finds it difficult to believe. To Mara, Ima has always been the stern taskmaster, the strong one who keeps the household running smoothly. What could possibly reduce *her* to tears?

Then she hears the words come tumbling out of Hannah's mouth: "O, Mara, Mara, why did you do it? We thought for certain we had lost you."

Mara opens her mouth to reply, but the words refuse to form themselves. All that comes out is meaningless sound. Her once-nimble tongue has become useless. A floodtide of helplessness engulfs her as she closes her eyes and drifts back into unconsciousness.

When she next opens her eyes, the morning light is filtering into the room. As she scans her surroundings, it dawns on her that she has been moved to the upper chamber on the roof of their house, a room normally reserved for guests. Her mother is still there. She has been dozing on the floor nearby, but as soon as she hears Mara stirring, she comes over and gently takes Mara's listless hands into her own.

"I will bring you something to eat," she announces. From the tone of her voice, Mara knows that, even if she had the power of speech, there would be no refusing her mother's offer.

While awaiting her return, Mara drags her legs across the mat and over the ledge and pulls herself to a sitting position. Suddenly she feels as if the room is rocking and swaying around her, and she drops back onto the mat, her eyes filling with tears of despair. In just a few hours, her whole life seems to have crumbled to ruins. She is unable to rise or speak, and for all she knows, a Roman soldier may have taken advantage of her helplessness and left her unfit for any respectable man to marry, even if her body eventually recovers.

Then all at once she realizes that in her dismay she has completely lost sight of her meeting with Yeshua. It had lasted only a moment, but in that moment he had seen her as a ray of unselfish love and had made her feel worthy and blessed. Soon afterward a soldier had seen her merely as an object to be used for his own selfish ends and had left her with this terrible bitterness. Bitter. She knows that is the literal meaning of the name *Mara*. But she has never before had reason to believe it actually applied to her. Oh, if only Yeshua's view, and not this bitterness, can be the one to prevail in her life and shape her future, impossible as that may seem at this moment.

When Ima returns with a small loaf of bread, a bowl of broth and some raisins from last autumn's grape harvest, Mara nibbles and sips as best she can, but she has no desire for food. What she really wants from her mother is to learn what happened after she lost consciousness.

Ima is anything but conversational as she coaxes Mara into eating, but after she realizes Mara has had her fill for the present, the story at last begins to unfold.

"Do you remember, Mara, the day you went chasing after a runaway lamb in the marketplace?" Ima asks her.

Mara nods. Even though she was just a tiny girl at the time, she will never forget that day. She had been separated from her mother in the surging crowds for a terrifyingly long stretch of time.

"Well, yesterday was the first time since then that I have felt the same dreadful panic," her mother explains. "You must have left during the afternoon, but only after it began to grow dark did I realize that you were not with your father. He went immediately to seek Nathan's help. Somehow Nathan seemed to know what direction you had taken. Had you told him where you were going?"

Mara shakes her head.

Ima continues, "Partway across the Kidron Valley, they saw you struggling with a Roman soldier. They saw you fall. When the soldier caught sight of them running toward you, he disappeared into the shadows."

Mara's relief in learning that the soldier had not had his way with her is quickly cut short by her mother's agonized outburst. "But, Mara," and at this point Ima's tears start flowing again, "Mara, what if they had not come at that very moment? How could you put yourself in such terrible danger?"

Mara can give no articulate answer, but she reaches out to her mother and holds her close until her sobs have ebbed away.

For most of the day, Mara drifts out of and back into consciousness. More often than not, Ima is there to see to her needs when she opens her eyes, bathing her face in cool water, bringing her food and drink. Never before has she felt so deeply the extent of her mother's love for her.

It is not until late in the afternoon, however, that her beloved Abba is finally able to come to her, and even then only briefly. When he appears, the expression on his craggy face is anything but comforting. She well knows that he might wish to ask her what she had been attempting to do yesterday afternoon and is almost grateful that circumstances prevent her from replying. She soon discovers, however, that she is not the cause of his agitation.

"I imagine you can guess why I could not come to you sooner," he begins somewhat hesitantly.

With her finger, Mara begins to outline the name "Y-E-S-H-U-A."

"You are right," he tells her.

For several moments, silence seems to hang darkly in the air between them. Mara tugs on his sleeve to urge him to tell her more.

Gravely, Eleazar relates what he knows. "He was teaching in the Temple again today, but, of course, any attempt to arrest him there could have caused violent protest. Caiaphas and his supporters tried more than once to trap him with a question, and each time he answered with another question that put them to silence."

Picturing the scene, Mara feels a fragile sliver of a smile flit across her face, but her father quickly brings her back to the harsh reality of the present. "Mara, they may have been silenced for the moment, but they are still powerful men. And late today they gained the one advantage they still lacked. Judas Iscariot, one of Yeshua's closest followers, has accepted their offer of thirty pieces of silver to lead them to his secret hiding place."

Mara is incredulous. How could anyone who had known and worked closely with Yeshua even dream of betraying him? And for thirty pieces of silver, the price of a slave! She imagines Caiaphas gloating and then feels the blood begin rushing to her face.

"Please try to be calm, little one," her father implores her. "At this point, the only thing we can do is pray. Perhaps the Romans will not be convinced by the charges of treason. We must wait ... and hope."

He squeezes her hand and exits the room, leaving her mind echoing with that little word "hope." If only she could find a way to catch hold of it.

10

Evening of the following day

Every year of her life for as long as Mara can remember, Passover has been a time of joyous celebration. Family members have always gathered together for the Seder. They would retell the awe-inspiring story of the exodus from Egypt and dine on a meal of bitter herbs, lamb, wine, and unleavened bread. Before and after the meal, they would recite the psalms of the *Hallel*. Every part of the Passover feast, from the meal preparation to the concluding prayer, has always brought gladness to Mara's heart—gladness to be among the Lord's people.

But today's melancholy efforts to celebrate the Passover are made all the sadder by those happy memories. By comparison, this Seder feels like an empty husk.

Her father has carried Mara down from the upper room so that she can join her parents for the meal. She lies helplessly on her mat, watching her mother prepare the festive dishes alone, for once wishing that she could help her. Ima's lone labors only intensify Mara's painful awareness of her injuries and of the absence of her sister Rachel's kindly assistance.

When at last she and her parents are reclining around the table together, Eleazar does his best to lead his family through the familiar ritual of the Passover Seder, but it is clear that his heart is not in it. Mara yearns to comfort him. But it is all she can do to take a few bites from each course that her mother brings to the table—not because she has any appetite but because she knows how deeply it would distress her parents if she did not.

After the meal and the final prayer, Mara finds herself drifting off to sleep to the hushed tones of Eleazar and Hannah's conversation. Suddenly, she is jolted awake by loud knocking at the courtyard door. It is Nathan, whom she has not seen since their disagreement over Yeshua and the Sanhedrin. She is ashamed that he should see her in this pitiful state, but it quickly becomes clear that he has not come to see *her*, but her father.

"Forgive me, Rabbi, for barging in at this late hour," he says, "but your presence is required immediately at the house of Caiaphas. My father is already on his way. There is to be a trial."

"They have arrested him then?" Eleazar asks.

Nathan looks anxiously toward Mara and whispers, "Yes."

After her father has left, Hannah asks Nathan to return Mara to the upper room so that she can get some rest. Gently he carries her on his shoulders like an injured lamb. He says nothing until he has settled her on her mat, but then he turns to her and asks, "You were trying to warn him, weren't you, Mara?"

She nods dejectedly.

"I was almost certain of it," he tells her. "That is how I knew where to search for you. But I blame myself for not anticipating your plan. I should have known. I should never have left you alone that afternoon."

Mara holds up her right palm and shakes her head, denying his assertion.

"Did you ever get to speak to him?" Nathan asks.

Again Mara nods, wishing with all her heart that she could speak to Nathan and tell him what Yeshua had said to her.

"Then at least you know that he was not left in ignorance—that he knows exactly what he is doing," Nathan observes in a vain effort to comfort her.

Yet again she nods, stifling her tears.

After Nathan has left, she lets them flow. Yeshua's words keep returning to her: "Do you truly believe that these men have the power to defeat my Father's purpose?" The answer, of course, is no. But she can hardly believe it would *serve* His purpose to silence the voice of Yeshua. It would be like silencing His *own* voice. Yet now that Yeshua has been arrested, that silencing seems all but inevitable.

All Mara can do is hold fast to Yeshua's assurance that "my Father—our Father—is wholly in charge." Never has that conviction been more difficult for her to cling to than it is this night.

11

The following day

After a night of fitful sleep, Mara wakens with a sense that something is terribly wrong. She cannot suppress the feeling that Yeshua is at this very moment in mortal danger. If only her father were here. Surely he would know what has befallen him.

When her mother brings her breakfast, she attempts to mouth the word *Abba*.

"Your father has gone out again, Mara," Hannah informs her. "It was nearly daybreak when he returned from the trial, and he stayed here only long enough for a very brief rest. I wish I could understand what is on his mind," she adds with a sigh.

So there is nothing for Mara to do but wait ... wait and try her best to keep her hopes alive. After a while, she falls asleep again, and when she awakens, it is as dark as night. She begins to wonder whether she has slept through the entire day until, to her surprise, her mother arrives with her noonday meal. Not until mid-afternoon does the sun reappear, and not until evening does Eleazar at last return home.

When he appears at the door of the upper room where Mara has been resting, his face is grave. For a long moment he simply stands there with his eyes closed, inhaling deeply.

At last, with his gaze on the floor, he begins, "What I have to tell you, Mara, is not easily spoken of. It will only add to your present sorrow, and I am not even certain that I fully understand it. The worst of it is that I have been obliged to take part in this outrage." Then he looks at her and asks, "Can you forgive me?"

She reaches out her arms to him, and he comes to her. Although Abba has always shown his love for his daughters through his eyes and through his words, his sense of dignity and propriety has, until now, made him hesitate to embrace them. But in this moment, as Mara somehow understands, he needs to be embraced, and in that embrace he can say what must be said without meeting her gaze, held in the circle of her love.

From the great, shaggy head leaning against her shoulder come the words, "I will begin with the worst—though you have probably guessed it. The deed is done. They have killed him. Yes, by crucifixion. And I have witnessed the whole ordeal, not out of curiosity but because I knew my Mara would want to be told exactly what had happened to Yeshua."

For his sake Mara stifles her tears and holds him closer. He continues, "Pontius Pilatus, the Roman governor, wanted nothing to do with the case. He tried everything possible to avoid sentencing him, believing him innocent of any crime. But to thwart the Sanhedrin when thousands of Jews are gathered here for Passover could, quite possibly, have cost him his position, so he finally gave them what they wanted."

At this point her father lifts his head and looks into her eyes. "But, Mara, I am not at all certain that they really got what they wanted. I have seen crucifixions before, but never one like this.

In spite of all that was done to him—and I am certain you do not wish me to describe it—Yeshua did not act the role of a victim. Through the whole ordeal, he seemed to have a higher purpose in mind. Nothing the Romans did to him could extinguish it." Eleazar pauses, a faraway look in his eyes.

Mara tugs on his sleeve, urging him to tell her more.

"I was close enough to hear some of the words he spoke from that cross," he continues. "He told a man on one of the other crosses—for two others were crucified with him—that today he would be with him in paradise. Then, later on, he asked one of his disciples—the only one who stayed with him through it all—to care for his mother as if she were his own. He even asked his heavenly Father to forgive those responsible for his execution, saying that they did it in ignorance. Imagine! He was able to forgive them even as this nightmare was going on."

At this point Eleazar, who has been on his knees since Mara took him into her arms, settles himself in a sitting position on the floor beside her. "I am grateful to be able to tell you that for Yeshua the suffering lasted only half a day. It must have been through the Lord's mercy. I have known of others who endured the agony of the cross for several days and nights. But Yeshua expired mid-afternoon after committing his spirit to the Lord."

In spite of her efforts to contain them, Mara's eyes begin to fill with tears. "Believe me, Mara. It was a blessing," her father tries to assure her. "The first day of the Feast of Unleavened Bread, which, of course, is a High Sabbath, began at sundown today. Those bodies had to be removed from the crosses in time for the bearers to purify themselves from the uncleanness of the dead before the Sabbath began. The other two victims were still alive, so their legs were broken to hasten their deaths. But when they had determined that Yeshua was already dead, his legs were left intact."

This is small comfort to Mara, but she nods to encourage her father to tell her more.

"There is only one more thing to tell you," he says. "As you may know, the Romans sometimes leave the dead bodies of victims on the crosses for the carrion birds. But this was not Yeshua's fate. My friend Joseph asked the governor's permission to take his body away. He did so with the help of Nicodemus, and they have buried Yeshua in a tomb owned by Joseph—a new tomb at the edge of a garden. So at least he has a clean and secure resting place. And at least two members of the Sanhedrin have shown themselves to be his friends."

At this, Eleazar rises to his feet. He reaches down and takes Mara's hands. "Now, dear Daughter, I must rest. I cannot begin to tell you how deeply I regret what has happened today. But some things are simply inevitable. We must bear them as best we can. I pray that you may somehow recover your speech and your balance and your joy. I miss our conversations. So rest, dear Mara, and think of happier days."

In spite of his kind words, the closing of the door behind him feels to Mara like the sealing of a tomb.

12

Three days later

In later years, Mara would come to be grateful that she could remember so little of what happened to her in the three days that followed. She would hear from her mother about her repeated refusal of food and from her father about the day he found her collapsed on the floor with her tear-stained face turned toward the wall. But she would remember firsthand almost none of it. All she would recall was a feeling of impenetrable darkness—as if the lamp of her life had suddenly been snuffed out.

On the other hand, the encounter that was to bring an end to those days of darkness was to remain etched in her memory as vividly as if it had taken place only yesterday.

———◦◦◦———

Bright sunlight is streaming through the tiny window of the upper room and around the edges of its loosely fitting door. Its glow has awakened in Mara an unaccountable feeling of hope. She has even tried once or twice to rise to her feet, but the feeling of lightheadedness continues to keep her off balance. Nevertheless, she is sitting on her mat with her legs dangling over the ledge when suddenly the door is thrown open and her father steps into the room, his bearded face flushed with excitement.

"I am so glad to see you sitting up, Mara," he says with a smile. Then he announces with unconcealed joy, "You have a visitor. I met her in the Temple. She has some remarkable news to tell you." And with that, he exits the room as suddenly as he had entered.

No sooner has he left than a woman appears in the doorway. Her shawl conceals the lower half of her face, and Mara has no idea who she might be. But when she lets the shawl drop to her shoulders, Mara gazes at her in amazement. Her visitor is none other than the woman Mara had spoken to months ago in Solomon's portico—Mary from Magdala in Galilee.

Mary crosses the room and seats herself beside Mara on the ledge, gently enfolding Mara's hands in her own. For a few moments she says nothing at all. She simply looks into Mara's eyes with a radiant warmth that reminds her of Yeshua.

Then slowly, quietly the words begin to come. "Mara, I have news of Yeshua."

In her excitement, Mara feels the dizziness beginning to worsen, but she remains upright on the ledge, all the while holding tightly to Mary's hands to keep her balance.

"I went to his tomb before sunrise this morning," Mary begins. "And when I reached it, I found that the stone protecting the entrance had been rolled back. I was certain it had been moved by grave robbers, and I was terribly upset." Her words begin to pour out faster. "I ran to find Peter and John, who were always so close to him, knowing they would want to hear what had happened. They returned to the tomb with me." Mary closes her eyes for a moment as if trying to picture the scene. "By then it was light enough for us to see inside, and we could scarcely believe our eyes. The grave clothes were neatly folded together as if someone had taken special care with them. But there was no sign of the body. We hardly knew what to make of it."

In spite of her lightheadedness, Mara hangs on Mary's every word.

"After the men had left," she continues, "I stood alone outside the tomb, weeping. Then I began to wonder if my eyes had deceived me, and I looked inside the tomb once more." Mary pauses for a moment. "This second look felt different somehow. I could feel an invisible—but perfectly tangible—presence right there where the body had lain. It was ... an angelic presence, not a gloomy one. In fact, it even questioned why I was weeping. But I was not yet ready for its message. At that moment, it seemed to me that I had every reason to weep."

Mary disentangles her hands from Mara's and wraps a steadying arm around her shoulders.

"When I came out into the garden again, a man was standing there—the gardener, or so I assumed. He, too, asked me why I was weeping. Thinking he might be the one who had removed the body, I begged him to tell me where he had taken it. All this while, of course, I had kept my eyes modestly downcast in the presence of this stranger. So you can imagine my amazement when he spoke my name: 'Mary.'" She pauses for a moment before revealing, in a voice just above a whisper, "But it was not the voice of a stranger, Mara. It was Yeshua's voice."

Mara lets out an inarticulate cry of joy. Then tears begin to flow.

"When I looked up, there he was, standing right beside me." Mary has to stop to wipe her eyes and take a few deep breaths. "At that moment, seeing him alive, I knew that I should have been expecting this all along—knowing him, knowing the Father. It seemed so natural, so right. Had he not raised Lazarus? Had he not said that in three days he would raise up the temple that had been destroyed?"

Mara remembers her own struggle in recent days to believe Yeshua's words about his Father's invincible purpose and wishes she could express the sympathy and admiration she feels for this steadfast follower of Yeshua.

Mary dabs at her eyes again before continuing. "I felt so ashamed of my doubts, but he uttered not one word of rebuke. He did not want me to touch him, however. It was as if he had reached a point where earth could not reclaim him, even though for a brief time he was walking upon it again." Mary pauses for a moment. "I do not think he will stay here for long. He asked me to tell the brethren that he would ascend to his Father—*our* Father. I have told as many of them as I was able to locate. But, Mara, some of the brethren had already *left* Jerusalem, so certain were they of Yeshua's end.

"By this afternoon, after I had spoken to those I could find, I felt drawn to the Temple, longing to give thanks at the evening prayer. There I recognized your father in the crowd." She smiles. "His noble height and his long beard make me think of Moses and the prophets. When I saw that you were not with him, I could not let formalities hold me back. I went straight up to him and asked after you. In his sorrow, he poured out the story of the Roman soldier, of your injuries. When I told him what I had witnessed in the garden this morning, he urged me to come and tell you about it myself."

Again Mary looks into Mara's eyes and gently brushes away her tears. "But, Mara, I do not believe that I have been sent here today only to tell you this good news and then leave you as I found you. The power that restored Yeshua is as potent in this room as it was in his tomb." Then, in a quiet but authoritative voice, she adds, "In Yeshua's name, dear Mara, stand."

Slowly, carefully, Mara rises to her feet. The room no longer seems to be swirling around her. She stands rooted to the spot for a moment, as stable as a cedar tree. Then she takes a step, then another. Her heart is so full of awe and gratitude that the words, "Oh, Mary, thank you!" are out of her mouth before she has time to realize that these are the first she has uttered since her encounter with Yeshua nearly a week before.

Mary shakes her head. "I am not the one you should be thanking, Mara."

Mara beams down at Mary, who is peacefully sitting in what for days has been the place of Mara's torment. "Oh, I have not forgotten Him, Mary. I will be thanking Him for the rest of my days. But it was you who opened my life to His light."

Mary gets up and takes Mara into her arms. "Since Yeshua did that for me," she whispers, "my life has never been the same."

"I truly believe that, Mary. In fact, I am certain of it because of what happened the last time I saw Yeshua. Can you guess what my errand was when the soldier assaulted me?"

"Had you gone looking for Yeshua?" Mary asks.

"Yes," Mara replies with a self-deprecating laugh. "I thought it my duty to warn him to leave Jerusalem. Imagine! But he did not rebuke me either. What he saw was a pure offering of love. For the first and only time in my life, I felt ... holy."

"Oh, Mara," Mary exclaims, "what a blessing your life will be if you will only let it!"

"I hope so," Mara sighs. "But I certainly do not expect to do works like Yeshua's."

Mary holds her at arm's length and looks into her eyes. "What do you think Yeshua would say to that, Mara? Does he do those works just so that his followers will stand in awe of him? Does he not expect them to ... well, *follow* him?"

Mara reflects for a moment. "I remember what he told us in Solomon's portico the day I met you: 'All that I do is the work of my Father. I do nothing of myself.'"

"Exactly. So why base your expectations on your opinion of *yourself*? Just be a willing channel for the Father when the moment comes. Do you think I came here today expecting to perform some great miracle?" Mary gazes at the newly restored young woman standing before her. "Of course not! But after what I saw in the garden this morning, it seemed only natural that His light should continue to stream through."

"You make it sound so easy, Mary," Mara observes, "but I am afraid it is not."

"You are right, Mara," Mary agrees. "It is simple, but certainly not easy. We must let go of so much of the load we carry around with us—so much of what we mistakenly think about ourselves and one another. But are you ready to begin?"

Mara smiles at Mary somewhat sheepishly. "If not today, when would I be?"

"Good," Mary responds. "I must go now and see if I can find any more of the brethren."

"Oh, may I come with you?" Mara asks eagerly.

"Has the Father not given you sufficient work to do here, Mara?" Mary scolds gently. Then she embraces her once more before draping her shawl around her head and shoulders and taking her leave.

13

Afterwards

For some time after Mary's departure, Mara stands stock still, trying to etch into her memory the moment that she is beginning to see as her own "resurrection." She dreads the thought that it could somehow sink out of sight beneath the mundane details of daily life. But she feels encouraged as she recalls Mary telling her that her life would be a blessing. She remembers all too well, however, the condition attached to that promise. "If you will let it," Mary had said. "Let" does not sound at all easy to strong-willed Mara. Or is "strong-willed" just part of that "load" she has been carrying—one of the things she needs to let go of? Perhaps so, but how? One day, she hopes, she will know.

Mara is suddenly aware that the light is fading in the upper room—her rooftop retreat—and that Hannah is undoubtedly in the process of preparing the evening meal downstairs. She remembers Ima's constant care for her through those dark days. The thought of her preparing yet another meal alone suddenly becomes unthinkable to Mara. Her mother's need, which to her had always seemed an unwelcome call to duty, now appears in an entirely different light. However humble, it is an opportunity to bless. She slips her outer garment over her tunic and hastens down the courtyard stairs and into the house.

It had not occurred to Mara to wonder whether, in parting, Mary had said anything to her parents about their daughter's recovery, but from the look on her mother's face as Mara walks through the door, it is clear that she had not. The knife Hannah has been holding clatters on the earthen floor as she stares in astonishment at her daughter.

"Mara!" she exclaims, rushing to her side. "You should not have come down those stairs alone. You might have fallen and injured yourself even worse. Sit down and rest."

"But, Ima, I came down to help you prepare our supper," says Mara, suppressing a smile.

Hearing her speak, her mother gasps and puts her hand over her mouth. Then tears of relief begin to flow as it dawns on her that her daughter is as sound as she has ever been. She nearly crushes her in her arms, repeating over and over, "Thank the Lord. Thank the Lord."

When the tide of excitement has ebbed, her mother holds her at arm's length and looks into her eyes. "Nathan told us you went out to warn Yeshua. I hope you will never again put yourself at risk that way, Mara."

"I hope I will never again feel that I must, Ima," she responds. Then she admits, "As it turned out this time, my warning was not really needed. Yeshua paid it no heed. But, Ima, he understood that it was given out of love. He valued that."

"As he well should!" her mother responds. And for the moment, Mara does not try to make her see anything more than common humanity in Yeshua's affirmation of her worth. It is a conversation for which neither of them is prepared.

All at once Mara becomes acutely aware of her father's absence. "Where is Abba?" she asks. "Did he go out again after bringing Mary up to me?"

"Yes. He has gone to discuss something with Joseph," Ima replies. Mara can well imagine what it is. "Now tell me, Mara, who is this Mary? Is she some kind of miracle worker?"

"She would not call herself that, Ima, but after she saw Yeshua alive this morning, seeing me whole seemed perfectly natural to her—an absolute certainty, in fact."

Her mother sighs. "I do not pretend to understand it. I just thank the Lord that you are standing here and talking with me."

By the time Eleazar returns home, Mara and Hannah are happily at work in the kitchen together, chattering like two affectionate sisters. Mara has never seen such joy in her father's face. But he does not seem nearly as surprised at her restored well-being as her mother had been.

Once they are at table together, however, he cannot refrain from asking her, "So, when did this blessed transformation take place, Mara? May I hazard a guess?"

"Of course," she responds with a smile.

"Could it have occurred during Mary's visit?" he asks, his bushy eyebrows raised above his twinkling eyes.

"How did you know, Abba?"

"When I let her into that room, she was positively luminous. I knew she would do you good."

"Being with her felt almost like being with Yeshua," Mara tells him.

"I can well imagine," says Eleazar. Then, with a slightly roguish grin, he observes, "And her presence seems to have similar effects."

"Oh, she would never agree with that suggestion, Abba," Mara asserts confidently. "Like Yeshua, she would view the effects entirely as the Father's work."

Eleazar looks across the table into the face of his newly restored daughter. "Yes, of course," he agrees. And casting his eyes heavenward, he adds, "Who else's?"

14

Six weeks later

Mara is beginning to wonder why she has chosen the rooftop as her workroom this morning. The summer heat has begun its descent on Jerusalem, and up here she is in full sun. But from up here Jerusalem sings out its presence to her. She has grown to love this city of hers—all of it, from the bellowing of its street vendors to the majesty of its Temple. On a cloudless day like this one, Jerusalem is a marvel of beauty and complexity—just the thing to inspire her as she grinds this newly harvested barley into flour.

She and her mother have been especially busy lately, storing up supplies to last during Mara's absence. It should be her mother who is making the journey, but nearly a month ago she had come down with a fever. Mara had cared for her just as Hannah had for Mara during her week of darkness. Beyond that, Mara had *prayed* for her mother, hoping to let in the light for her as Mary had for Mara on the day of her remarkable recovery. But she had felt woefully inadequate. Her desire to restore Ima to health was so keen that she was urgently pleading with the

Father—as though she could will Him into healing her mother —instead of simply opening her heart to His power and grace. In time, the fever had run its course. For that, at least, she could be grateful.

Then one day Hannah had spoken to her of Rachel. Her time of delivery was only a few weeks off. She would need help in the days following the birth of her child, and Hannah was still too weak to make the journey or bear the summer heat of Jericho. Mara had not waited to be asked. It was too good an opportunity to bless Rachel, and the thought of being with her sister again filled her with joy.

Just last week, arrangements were made for her to undertake the daylong journey to Jericho with a group of travelers leaving Jerusalem after the upcoming Sabbath. Meanwhile, the necessary preparations must be completed so that Ima will be able to manage alone after her departure. So today Mara finds herself here on the rooftop at work with these grinding stones.

Street noises mask the footfalls on the courtyard steps, so she is startled at first when she becomes aware of a long, narrow shadow stretching across her line of vision and looks up to see Nathan standing in front of her. She has seen him only a few times since her recovery—brief encounters that afforded little opportunity for conversation. She welcomes the sight of him smiling down at her.

"Your mother told me you were at work up here," he explains.

"Yes. This view makes even barley grinding enjoyable— well worth carrying all this up to the roof," she says, pointing to the sack of barley and her millstones.

"You must be as strong as ever," Nathan states, more as a hopeful inquiry than a fact.

"Stronger, I think," Mara replies, pressing down and rotating the hand stone.

"What amazes me is that you actually seem *happy* doing this," Nathan comments, gesturing toward her work. "Have you had any time for your Torah studies lately?"

"Not as much as I would like," Mara replies, "but, strangely enough, I do not really see myself as a scholar these days."

"That *is* surprising," he observes. "Then how *do* you see yourself?" he asks, his curiosity piqued.

"It is not easy to explain. I still turn to the Scriptures each day, though often only to what I have written in here," she says, placing her hand over her heart. "What has changed is that now I do it more to satisfy a hunger than to gain knowledge."

"A hunger for what?" Nathan asks.

"For something that, only two months ago, I knew nothing about. I hunger to *see*—in the way Yeshua saw me the day I went to warn him, in the way Mary saw me the day I recovered." Mara sets down her hand stone for a moment. "I think there could be no greater blessing on earth."

Nathan is silent until she takes up her work again. "Can you actually see that way, Mara?" he asks.

"Not very clearly yet, but I feel that I am learning to," she answers. "You may not believe this, but truly I no longer resent having to do women's work. I have discovered that it is not drudgery when it is done out of love. How strange that I never saw that before!"

"And now—so your mother tells me—you will soon be doing it for your sister," Nathan remarks. "How long will you be in Jericho?"

"A month ... or perhaps a bit longer."

"When will you leave?"

"In four days, at sunrise."

"And I am told you will be traveling with a group of strangers."

"So it seems."

Nathan pauses for a moment, then looks down at her soberly. "That rocky area on the descent to Jericho can be treacherous, you know. Thieves conceal themselves behind those rocks. I would feel much less anxious—and I believe your parents would, too—if you would allow me to accompany you to Jericho that day."

"All the way to Jericho!" Mara exclaims. "But what about your studies?"

"They can wait a few days," Nathan assures her. "Besides, I have a cousin in Jericho whom I have not seen in nearly two years. We would both welcome a visit."

"Far be it from me to refuse such a kind offer," says Mara, beaming up at him.

But Nathan's eyes are avoiding hers, and he has an almost shy look on his face that Mara cannot remember seeing before. "Perhaps you overestimate my kindness, Mara. I may have a secretly selfish motive for wanting to make this journey with you."

Mara's mind takes a few unaccustomed twists and turns before she begins to grasp what he is hinting at. But partly to tease him and partly to be certain she has not misunderstood, Mara asks, "What selfish motive could my own near-brother possibly have in making such a kind offer?"

Nathan swallows hard and looks into her eyes. "Perhaps he is hoping that you will like journeying with him—maybe enough to make it a lifelong habit." He waits an awkward moment for her to speak. Then, stammering, he blurts out the question: "Is ... is that a possibility, do you think?"

Mara looks up into his expectant face. "If he asks me again next year, it just might be."

15

Jericho, ten days later, early morning

Mara sits in the shadow of her brother-in-law's house, hoping for a few cooling breezes. From here she can see in the distance the rocky hillside down which she and Nathan had traveled only a few days before.

She finds it difficult to imagine what the journey would have been like without him. Not only had he made every provision for her comfort, including a donkey to carry her bundle and at times herself, but he had also been excellent company, allowing sweet periods of quiet to intersperse their conversation, sensing when to stretch out his hand to help her and when not to. She had never before spent an entire day with him, and she now finds herself wishing she had given him more encouragement on the day of his awkward and unanticipated attempt at a marriage proposal. She had been caught off guard in part because she has always regarded Nathan as a brother, but now she realizes how quickly that could change.

The prospect of marriage is still daunting to her, however, especially in this moment when her sister is giving birth. Even from outside the house, she can hear Rachel's occasional moans during the final stages of her labor. An hour or so earlier, Rachel had asked her to wait outside until after her delivery. Mara knows why. Rachel is concerned that her suffering might cause Mara, the only woman in the room who had not experienced childbirth herself, to dread it. Uncomplaining as Rachel normally is, she clearly had not reckoned on the echoes of her birth pangs escaping through the windows of the house. Although her sister is surrounded by capable women—her mother-in-law, sister-in-law, and a midwife of long experience —Mara cannot help wishing she could be there to comfort her.

Her sympathy for Rachel is diverted by another person emerging from the house. It is Matthias, her tall, gaunt brother-in-law, who is usually calm and unruffled. At this moment, however, his hand is on his forehead and his brows are in an anguished knot. When he sees Mara, he appears surprised and a little embarrassed. "I just want this to be over," he remarks.

"So do I," says Mara, searching for something comforting to say. "The first birth is always the hardest, or so I am told."

"I certainly hope so," he replies. "I could not bear to see her go through something this painful every year or two—all because of me."

"Oh, Matthias," says Mara, feeling a sudden rush of warmth for this brother-in-law she has hardly had a chance to get acquainted with. "You could only feel this way if you love her. Do you realize what a blessing that is for you both?"

Matthias says nothing, but shrugs his shoulders and looks into her eyes with a sigh and a weary smile.

"Believe it or not," Mara continues, "it is even a blessing for me. On your wedding day, I was mystified by Rachel's happiness. I wanted to postpone my own marriage as long as possible." Beaming him a smile, she adds, "Now I have at least some idea of what might make it ... quite bearable."

Mara stands and motions to Matthias, and together they circle the dusty courtyard together until the sharp, high cry of an infant rings out from inside the house.

Just as they burst through the door, they hear the midwife call out, "A boy!" Knowing that no man may enter the birthing room, Mara looks up at Matthias apologetically as she heads in that direction. But Matthias is smiling. A son! What greater blessing could he wish for?

When Mara enters, the other women are busily occupied with Rachel, who is still squatting on the birthing stones, supported by Matthias's mother and sister, as the midwife assists her with the afterbirth. Meanwhile a tiny, red, animated bundle of humanity lies wriggling on a pillow nearby, squalling out his high-pitched protests to an unfamiliar world.

"May I bathe him?" asks Mara in an effort to be helpful.

"Yes," replies the preoccupied midwife, more to get her out of the way, Mara suspects, than to avail herself of her help. "But be sure to support his head."

Mara lifts the slippery little body from the pillow and holds him against her chest to keep him from wriggling out of her grasp. She carries him across the room to a basin of water just below the west window. Gently lowering him into it, she goes to work, wiping his pink round face with a sea sponge. Once his face is clean, she pauses for a moment just to look at it. He quiets down and opens his eyes, and in this moment her tiny nephew becomes, to her surprise, unexplainably precious to her —a gift from the great Giver of life.

She begins to sponge off his tiny limbs and smiles at their perpetual motion as they wiggle and twist every which way. It is only then that she notices to her sorrow that his right arm, unlike the left one, is hanging limply at his side.

Mara feels a deep protest welling up. How wrong it seems for this little one to begin life this way! If only she could—even for a moment—*see* him the way Yeshua would. As if in answer to her longing, the first full ray of afternoon sunlight streams through the window above the basin, and suddenly the newborn child is awash in light. Tears spring to Mara's eyes. Tears of gratitude for the powerful, loving Presence that has brought this child into being and is even now filling this very room with His blessings. Tears of remorse for having believed what her eyes were telling her more than what her love of Him is now showing her.

Seeing her little nephew in the light of that love, Mara wipes the tears from her face and continues with her task. By the time the midwife crosses the room to begin wrapping the swaddling clothes around the babe's tiny body, Mara notices that his right arm is wiggling around as vigorously as the other. She can hardly contain her joy as she turns to embrace her sister.

16

Several weeks later

As she folds and packs her few belongings, Mara can scarcely believe the day has come for her return to Jerusalem. Her stay in Jericho has been too occupied with household tasks for her to give much thought to her life back home. But somehow she has found time each day to be with her little nephew, holding him, rocking him, singing to him.

To her surprise, Rachel and Matthias had asked her on the day of his birth what name she thought they should give him. Of course, Mara could think of no name more worthy than "Yeshua," and she had blurted it out without much hope that they would choose it. However, it happened to be the name of Matthias's paternal grandfather, and they embraced the idea immediately. So little Yeshua, already so dear to her, had become dearer still with the addition of his name.

Mara can hardly wait to hear what her father thinks of it. She is looking forward to being with Abba and Ima again and telling them about their new grandson. But will she be able to tell them

—her father, at least—of the wonder she witnessed on the morning of Yeshua's birth?

So far she has not found words to share it even with Rachel. It feels like a secret between her and the Father—a precious flame around which she must cup her hands to protect it from the harsh winds of this world. But she has no doubt that someday it must be told. How ungrateful she would be if she kept silent about it. Perhaps the time to speak of it will be during Matthias and Rachel's visit to Jerusalem next month to make the customary offering at the Temple forty days after the birth of their son.

Through a west-facing window, Mara can see in the distance a man approaching. He is riding on a donkey. The sight reminds her of the afternoon, a few days before Passover, when Yeshua had ridden into Jerusalem. How different her expectations had been then. She, like hundreds of others in the crowd, had been hoping for a Messiah who would set their people free from Roman domination. But the freedom Yeshua had been offering them was not political. In fact, it was of a very different nature than most of them had ever imagined—a freedom that would take root *within* them if they let it. It was the freedom of his Father's kingdom—the freedom he had been living right there in the midst of them.

Already she has felt it beginning to take root within her, working out of sight like leaven, lifting and lightening her view of life. She now feels ready to face whatever the future might hold for her. And she will not be at all surprised—or disappointed—if she ends up doing so with the young man who is now approaching on that donkey, ready and more than willing to ease her journey back to Jerusalem.

APPENDIX

Chapter 1

Bible references:

• Exodus 14:15-31

Discussion questions:

1. How do Mara's aspirations differ from her sister's? What sets her apart from most Jewish women of her time?

2. What reasons might a Jewish man of that period have had for preferring sons to daughters? Where do we still see traces of that tendency today?

3. Why do you think Mara, who for years has loved the *stories* in the Scriptures, has only recently begun to appreciate the *laws*? What do you think it takes to appreciate the laws?

Chapter 2

Bible references:

- Deuteronomy 6:4-9
- Leviticus 23:39-43
- Matthew 14:15-21/Mark 6:35-44/Luke 9:12-17
- Exodus 20:8-11
- Leviticus 11:9-12
- Exodus 30:17-21
- Leviticus 15:2, 11
- Deuteronomy 21:1-9
- Matthew 15:1-20/Mark 7:1-23
- Micah 5:2
- Matthew 5:17
- John 7:2, 14-52
- John 8:28-58

Discussion questions:

1. Why do you think holidays and traditions have such an important role in the life of Mara's family?

2. According to the Gospels, how was Jesus received by the people of his own era? Why might he have drawn a different group of listeners than did the Pharisaic rabbis? What do you think might have interested these listeners in hearing him?

3. Why do you think the Pharisees wanted to discredit him? How did they attempt to do it?

Chapter 3

Bible references:

- John 5:1-9

Discussion questions:

1. Why do you think the Romans allowed the Jews to have a Temple and to continue worshipping there?

2. What impact do you think Jesus' healing works might have had on his credibility as a teacher?

Chapter 4

Bible references:

- John 10:22-39

- John 9:1-7

- Matthew 13:33/Luke 13:20, 21

- Psalm 82:6

- Luke 8:1, 2

- Acts 5:36, 37

Discussion questions:

1. Why do you think Jesus could so confidently affirm the presence of God's kingdom even in the shadow of a Roman fortress?

2. Why do you think the tradition that Mary Magdalene was a

woman of bad reputation got started in the early church even though it has no basis in the Scriptures?

3. How do you think it would have felt to be a member of the Sanhedrin and at the same time a follower of Jesus?

Chapter 5

Bible references:

• John 11:1-44

Discussion questions:

1. What reasons might a young woman of this era have had either to hope for or to dread marriage?

2. What do you think your expectation would have been if you'd been in the crowd outside Lazarus's tomb? Why?

3. Do you agree with Mara's view of what might keep others from healing as Jesus did? Why or why not?

Chapter 6

Bible references:

• John 3:1-10

Discussion questions:

1. What are the factors that contribute to Mara's frustration? Do you think Jesus' teachings could have helped in this situation? If so, how?

2. Although many of the Pharisees opposed Jesus, what was there about their approach to life that made some of them, like Joseph and Nicodemus, gravitate toward him?

3. What do you think it takes to be "born of the Spirit"? How can you know when you have been? What would change after this kind of rebirth?

Chapter 7

Bible references:

- Exodus 12:1-14
- John 12:1, 2, 12-18 (Matthew 21:1-11/Mark 11:1-11/

  Luke 19:28-40)
- Zechariah 9:9
- Psalm 118:26
- John 11:47-50; John 12:42, 43

Discussion questions:

1. Why do you think the crowds gave Jesus such a hero's welcome on what we call Palm Sunday? What kind of Messiah were many of them hoping for?

2. What do you think may have been on Jesus' mind as he entered Jerusalem that day?

3. Do you think Jesus' supporters on the Sanhedrin could or should have done more to prevent his execution? Why or why not?

Chapter 8

Bible references:

- John 11:54
- Matthew 21:12-14/Mark 11:15-18/Luke 19:45-48

Discussion questions:

1. Why do you think Nathan's concerns are so different from Mara's?

2. Do you think Mara is justified in the action she takes? Why or why not?

3. Why do you think Mara is so moved by what Yeshua says about her? Have you ever gotten a similar message from someone you looked up to just when you needed to hear it?

Chapter 9

Bible references:

- Matthew 21:23-27/Mark 11:27-33/Luke 20:1-8
- Matthew 22:15-40/Mark 12:13-34/Luke 20:20-40
- Matthew 26:1-5, 14-16/Mark 14:1, 2, 10, 11/Luke 22:1-6

Discussion questions:

1. After her injury, what seems different about Mara's relationship with her mother? How do you account for the change? Have you ever experienced a similar change in your relationship with a family member?

2. How do the different ways Yeshua and the Roman soldier perceive her and treat her influence the way Mara feels about herself and her world?

3. How is Mara's outlook affected by the various reports her father gives her about Yeshua? Why do you think he seems hesitant to share them with Mara at first? Why do you think he goes ahead and tells her in spite of his hesitancy?

Chapter 10

Bible references:

- Exodus 12:18-28
- Matthew 26:57/Mark 14:53/Luke 22:54

Discussion questions:

1. Why do you think misfortunes can seem even more unbearable than usual at holiday times?

2. Why do you think Mara has difficulty believing that God's purpose for Yeshua will not be thwarted if he is arrested and crucified? What might her concept of that purpose be? What is your own concept of that purpose?

Chapter 11

Bible references:

- Luke 23:1-25 (Matthew 27:2, 11-24/Mark 15:1-15)
- John 18:28-40; John 19:1-16

- Luke 23:39-43; John 19:26, 27; Luke 23:34; Mark 15:33, 37
- John 19:31-42; Luke 23:50-54 (Matthew 27:57-60/
  Mark 15:42-46)

Discussion questions:

1. On the subject of Yeshua's crucifixion, Mara's father seems to be more in agreement with Pontius Pilate than with most of his fellow members of the Sanhedrin. But how might Eleazar's reasons for wanting to prevent the crucifixion differ from Pilate's?

2. What is there in Eleazar's report of the crucifixion that could be regarded as good news in the midst of all the bad? Why do you think the more positive news doesn't seem to register with Mara? With the hindsight we have today, would you say this good news was more significant than she could have realized? Why or why not?

Chapter 12

Bible references:

- John 20:1-18 (Mark 16:9-11)

Discussion questions:

1. Why do you think Jesus chose Mary Magdalene to be the first witness of his resurrection? Why would he have chosen a woman rather than one or more of his twelve disciples?

2. How do you think Mary's outlook may have been changed by witnessing the resurrection?

3. What do you think Mary means when she says that doing God's work is simple, but not easy? What do you think it takes?

Chapter 13

Discussion questions:

1. Why does Mara need to stand still for a time after Mary leaves her? What do you think she is hoping for? What do you think she fears?

2. What motivates Mara to get moving again? Is it more in line with her hopes or her fears? Why?

3. Do you notice any differences in the way she relates to her parents after her healing? Do you think these differences may be due to changes in her outlook? Why or why not?

Chapter 14

Discussion questions:

1. What changes do you see in Mara now that she's had time to reflect on her experiences with Yeshua and with Mary? In what ways does she still seem the same?

2. What has now become the primary purpose of Mara's study of the Scriptures? Is it important to you to study in the new way she studies? Why or why not?

Chapters 15

Discussion questions:

1. Compare Mara's current outlook on the role she must play as a woman in her society with her outlook of the previous year. What do you think could make such a transition possible?

2. How does Mara's prayer for her nephew differ from her prayer for her mother in Chapter 14? Why might that difference be significant?

Chapter 16

Bible references:

• Leviticus 12:2, 4, 6

Discussion questions:

1. What do you think makes Mara keep the healing of her nephew's arm a secret at first? What do you think makes her also feel that it must eventually be told?

2. What is your view of the freedom Jesus lived and modeled for mankind? Freedom from what? Freedom for what? How do you think such freedom is attained?

GLOSSARY

Abba and Ima. Aramaic words roughly equivalent to *Dad* and *Mom*, respectful but informal. Remember that in Jesus' time Jews living in Palestine spoke Aramaic.

Abraham. The first of three patriarchs—Abraham, his son Isaac, and his grandson Jacob/Israel—to whom Jews trace their ancestry. Abraham lived about 2,000 years before Jesus.

Adonai. A Hebrew word for God meaning "Master" or "Lord." It is used during prayer or Torah reading in place of the name for God that was given to Moses on Mt. Sinai and that, even today, many Jews consider too sacred to speak aloud. That sacred name is often written as YHWH or YHVH and pronounced "Yahweh" or "Yehovah." It is thought to be related to the Hebrew verb *to be*.

Hallel. The word means "praise" in Hebrew. The prayer of praise and thanksgiving known as the Hallel consists of Psalms 113-118 and is recited or chanted on Jewish holidays. Psalm 136, known as the Great Hallel, is recited after it at the Seder, the Passover meal.

HaShem. Hebrew for "the name." HaShem can be substituted for YHWH in conversation as Adonai is in prayer. (See *Adonai*.)

Hanukkah. Also known as the Festival of Lights and the Feast of Dedication, it is an eight-day holiday commemorating the rededication of the Temple at the time when the sons of the Jewish Maccabee family successfully led a rebellion against Antiochus IV, the Syrian king who had profaned the Temple. In 166 BC the Temple was purified and rededicated, but only one container of ritual oil had been left unprofaned—enough to light the menorah in the Temple for only one day. Miraculously, it burned for eight. To commemorate this, a nine-branched candelabrum called a *chanukiah* is lit during Hanukkah, the central wick being used to light an additional wick on each of the eight days of the festival.

Menorah. Once a seven-branched oil-lamp stand used in the Temple, it has become a universal symbol of Judaism in the form of a seven-branched candelabrum.

Passover and the Feast of Unleavened Bread. Passover, which is called *Pesach* in Hebrew, was one of three festivals during which Jews were expected to make a pilgrimage to the Temple in Jerusalem. (The other pilgrimage festivals were Shavuot [Pentecost or Feast of Weeks] and Sukkot [Tabernacles].) Passover commemorates the Israelites' escape from slavery in Egypt. It took ten plagues to finally convince Pharaoh to let them go. The tenth plague brought death to the firstborn of every Egyptian household, but the plague "passed over" the homes of the Israelites. In their need to leave Egypt in a hurry, they could not wait for the bread dough to rise. So to this day, during the eight days of the Passover festival, only unleavened bread is eaten.

Pharisees. A Jewish faction that set great importance on the strict observance of the Torah and rabbinical law. Along with the Sadducees, Pharisees constituted the Sanhedrin. Bible readers tend to remember them for their opposition to Jesus, but some of them were actually his supporters.

Rabbi. We think of a rabbi today as more or less the Jewish equivalent of a Christian pastor, but in Jesus' time the term *rabbi* or *master* was used to address a teacher of Torah, who was a scholar and mentor, rather than a man who officiated in formal religious worship.

Sabbath. The weekly Sabbath, a day of rest and worship, extends from sunset Friday to sunset Saturday. In obedience to the Fourth Commandment, Jews refrain from work on the Sabbath. During the year, in addition to the weekly Sabbaths, Jews celebrate seven High Sabbaths, which may or may not happen to coincide with a weekly Sabbath. The first day of the Feast of Unleavened Bread is one of these High Sabbaths. (See *Passover.*

Sadducees. An aristocratic class of priests who, along with some Pharisees, constituted the Sanhedrin. The Sadducees were responsible for performing the ritual sacrifices and other ceremonial duties at the Temple. They were more willing than the Pharisees to compromise with their Roman rulers. Unlike the Pharisees, they did not believe in resurrection after death. Caiaphas, the High Priest, was a Sadducee.

Sanhedrin. *Sanhedrin* means "council." The Great Sanhedrin, which was like a Jewish "Supreme Court," is the one mentioned in the Gospels. It consisted of 71 members from two parties that were sometimes in disagreement—the Pharisees and the Sadducees. Headed by the High Priest, the Sanhedrin convened daily—except for Sabbaths—in the Hall of Hewn

Stone adjacent to the Temple. By the time of Jesus' ministry, the authority of the Sanhedrin was curtailed by the Roman government.

Seder. A ritual feast marking the beginning of Passover.

Shavuot. Celebrated in late May or early June, Shavuot commemorates the day when God gave the Torah to the Israelites at Mt. Sinai. It is also known as Pentecost or the Feast of Weeks.

Shema. The word *shema* means "hear" (also "listen" and "obey") in Hebrew, and it is used to refer to a section of the Torah (Deuteronomy 6:4-9) that begins, "Hear, O Israel: the Lord is our God, the Lord is one." For Jews, this passage serves as a focal point of morning and evening prayers.

Sukkot. Referred to in the Gospels as "the Feast of Tabernacles," it is a seven-day autumn festival during which a Jewish family of Jesus' time would eat and sleep in a sukkah, a frail walled structure covered with palm fronds or leafy boughs, to commemorate their ancestors' living conditions during their forty years in the wilderness.

Tefillin. Also known as phylacteries, they are small leather boxes containing tiny scrolls with verses from the Torah. They have leather straps so they can be attached to the arm and forehead during prayer.

Torah. The written Law of Moses, consisting of the first five books of what Christians refer to as the Old Testament.

Yeshua. A word meaning "salvation," it is the Aramaic and Hebrew form of Joshua. In Greek the name is Iesous, which in English becomes Jesus.

Printed in Great Britain
by Amazon